This book is dedicated to J. C. den Hartog

Oceanographic Series™
Invertebrates: A Quick Reference Guide

First Printing June 2001
10 9 8 7 6 5 4 3

Published by Ricordea Publishing
Miami, Florida, USA

Distributed by Two Little Fishies, Inc.
4016 El Prado Blvd., Coconut Grove
Florida, 33133 USA

Printed and bound by Artes Graficas, Toledo S.A.
Design and production by Daniel N. Ramirez
Photographs by Julian Sprung except where noted otherwise
Back cover photo: Leon Corry

ISBN 1-883693-00-4

INVERTEBRATES

A Quick Reference Guide
by Julian Sprung

Book Design by Daniel N. Ramirez

Published by Ricordea Publishing
Miami, Florida 33133 USA

nvertebrates are animals without backbones. They include the simplest of creatures such as microscopic amoeba and protozoans, and highly complex ones like octopus. The distinction made between vertebrate and invertebrate animals on the basis of the absence of a nerve cord or spine is arbitrary, and does not reflect in any way the relatedness of the animals to each other, nor relative "position" in an imagined line of evolutionary complexity. While many invertebrates have common ancestors, others are only distantly related, and some invertebrate groups are more closely related to vertebrates than to other invertebrates. Nevertheless, it has been the historical practice of man to simplify the issue and just lump together animals without backbones as a distinct group from the vertebrates. Figures 1.1 and 1.3 show generally how the different groups are related to each other and how diverse they are (= relative number of species). Figure 1.2 shows how all living creatures are classified in a five kingdom system.

Of all animals, ones without backbones comprise about 95% of the known species. The oceans are teaming with invertebrates, but some live in freshwater and many, insects for example, have invaded the land and air. This book focuses on invertebrates found in the tropical marine environment, but even with this narrowed scope it cannot cover the range of forms found there. It is my intention to describe only macroscopic ones that are likely to be maintained in aquariums (or attempted at least). The texts in the bibliography offer further detail regarding microscopic forms, which are common in aquaria, and other invertebrates not commonly maintained in aquaria.

The nemertea, aschelminths, lesser protostomes, lophophorates, and hemichordata, all of which may be encountered in tropical reef aquaria, are not covered in this book. Likewise a tremendous number of creatures within the main groups covered are not featured either, for example in the arthropods: pycnogonida, amphipoda, isopoda, and mysidacea. Nevertheless, this book covers a wide range of conspicuous creatures likely to be encountered by anyone diving or exploring coral reef, seagrass, or mangrove areas around the world. It therefore is a useful field guide for the naturalist or diver. Future volumes of this series may include some of the aforementioned animals.

This second quick reference guide in the Oceanographic Series follows the quick reference style of offering identification and husbandry information with a minimum of text, along with the use of helpful diagrams and charts. Rather than load my descriptions with citations of references, I chose to keep the text as simple to read as possible and place the references I used plus other helpful texts in the bibliography at the end of the book. My intention is to allow the reader the ability to quickly determine whether the pictured invertebrate is useful, toxic, destructive, or harmful in some way, easy to maintain, delicate, suitable for his or her aquarium, or not suitable for the particular aquarium or captivity in general.

On that subject, some of the invertebrates featured in this book are completely unsuitable for typical home aquariums based on their dietary requirements, other special husbandry needs, or the fact that they are poisonous. I include them in this book because some are commonly or occasionally harvested and imported for the aquarium trade. It is my intention to point out that certain creatures should not be harvested, or that they should only be housed in aquaria when the aquarist makes the effort to meet their special requirements. These requirements may include a temperature range, feeding, or special environmental features such as size of the aquarium, or water flow engineering. Rather than be simplistic about the matter I have tried to be as specific as possible regarding the reasons, while still keeping true to the quick reference format. Please refer to the simple quick reference format I describe in the "How to use this book" pages.

Some of the featured creatures are parasites or pests that are common in reef aquariums despite many aquarists' attempts to eradicate them.. I offer tips about how to control them or, for those who may wish to maintain them for study, I offer information about how to properly care for them.

A few of the featured invertebrates with desirable attributes for aquariums are presently not commonly harvested or cultured for the aquarium trade, and it is my intention to promote their harvest or culture for aquariums. They may simply be elegant creatures or may have desirable functions such as the control of unwanted algae or the eradication of plague creatures such as *Aiptasia* anemones and flatworms.

I have grouped the animals with their nearest relatives into chapters and offer brief information about them in the introductory paragraph of each chapter. These introductions are meant as brief summaries of the group. Much more detailed information is available from the references given in the bibliography.

The identification of invertebrates is in many instances a simple matter, as some are quite distinctive. This is not always the case of course. The list of suggested readings is the resource from which I was able to identify most of the creatures, though at times I had to consult specialists within a particular group or friends of mine with a similar passion for marinelife. This is something I enjoy doing. By creating books such as this one I tie together an appreciation of diving and documenting creatures in their natural habitat with observing them in my own reef aquariums. I hope that my books inspire the reader to do the same, and share with other people new records of observations of natural history.

I wish to thank the following people who have assisted me in the creation of this book.

Phil Alderslade, Millie, Jean, Mabel, Nene, Ted, Edwin, Eddie, and the staff at All Seas Fisheries, Miami, Alladin Diver of Kushimoto, Japan, A-Pet, Chicago, Eduard Aulov (Cheeripaha), Marj Awai at the Florida Aquarium, Raoul Backhaus, Dominique Barthelemey at Oceanopolis, France, Kathleen Berg, Filippo Bertagniolio and Julie Schwenke of Corallarium, Milan, Alain Bertschy, Bruce Brande, Robert and Yael Brons, Carol Buchanan, Rob and Robin Burr, Dr. Bruce Carlson, Country Critters, New York, Helmut Debelius, Charles Delbeek, Jim and Cathy Duncan, Jean-Jacques Eckert, Exotic Aquariums, Miami, Fabrice, Yves, Bernard, Christian of TNT in Paris, and Bachir of course too. Stephane Fournier, Svein Fosså, Max Gibbs, Mitch Gibbs, Santiago Gutierrez, J. C. den Hartog, Rolf Hebbinghaus at the Löbbecke Museum, House of Fins, Connecticut, Jean Jaubert, Daphne Fautin, Ann Fielding and the crew of Spirit of Solomons, Roy and Teresa Herndon, Paul Humann, Larry Jackson, Daniel Knop, Rudi Kraus and Johannes Kirchhauser at Staatliches Museum für Naturkunde Abt. Vivarium Karlsruhe, Morgan Lidster of Inland Aquatics, Jeff Macare, Dr. Frank Maturo at the University of Florida, Jose Mendez, Yoshi Mizuno, Tony Nahacky, Alf Nilsen, Nadia Ounais and Pierre Gilles at the Musee Oceanographique de Monaco, Mike Paletta, Blane Perun, Vince Rado, Tom Smoyer, and Kelly at Harbor Branch, Reef International, Milan, Italy, Eric Reichardt, Reef and Fin, Connecticut, Jean-Claude and Marty Ringwald, Bill Rudman, Lluvitza Sagastegui who accompanied me on several photo "expeditions" in south Florida, David Saxby, Ed Sidell and Chris Ingram, Monterey Bay Aquarium, Greg Schiemer, Mike and Jan Sergy, Dave and Kathy Smith, Alan Storace, Brian and Ed Taimuty of Wet Pets and Friends, Pittsburg, Kenny Tan, Perry Tishgart, Koji Wada of Blue Harbor, Osaka, Japan, David Wrobel, who photographed the *Beroe* sp. Ctenophore, Copyright © 1990 Monterey Bay Aquarium Foundation, Peter Wilkens, Joe Yaiullo at Atlantis on Long Island, Jeremy Yong.

….and the many other aquarists, pet shop owners, and aquarium curators who have graciously allowed me to photograph their aquariums, and assisted me with the opportunity to document the rare creatures housed in them.

Thanks once again to my brother Elliot Sprung, who worked on the many images for this book under a very tight schedule and did a superb job, as usual.

Thanks to my family and friends for being patient while I was away travelling then "away" finishing the book then travelling then finishing the book. I will see you one of these days!

Thanks to Daniel Ramirez for making this yet another beautiful creation.

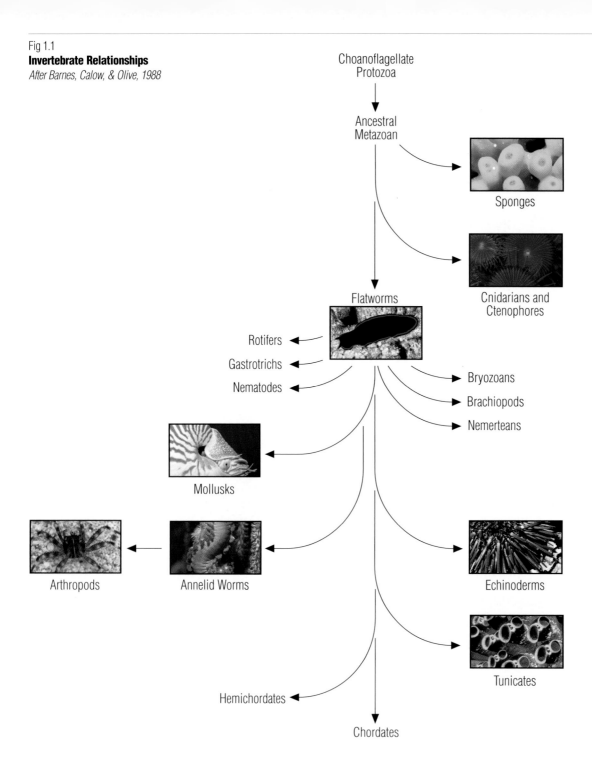

Fig 1.1
Invertebrate Relationships
After Barnes, Calow, & Olive, 1988

Choanoflagellate
Protozoa

Ancestral
Metazoan

Sponges

Cnidarians and
Ctenophores

Flatworms

Rotifers

Gastrotrichs

Nematodes

Bryozoans

Brachiopods

Nemerteans

Mollusks

Arthropods

Annelid Worms

Echinoderms

Tunicates

Hemichordates

Chordates

Fig 1.2
Five Kingdom System
After Barnes, Calow, & Olive, 1988

Although many people commonly think of living creatures as being either plants or animals, there are actually five distinct kingdoms of living creatures, the Monera, Protista, Animalia, Plantae, and Fungi. The diagram also separates unicellular creatures from multicellular, and distinguishes those having a cell nucleus and organelles, the Eukaryotes, from those lacking these features, the Prokaryotes. The small lobes between the animal, plant, and fungi kingdoms are meant to indicate that there are also creatures that don't easily fit into just one kingdom, having characteristics of at least two.

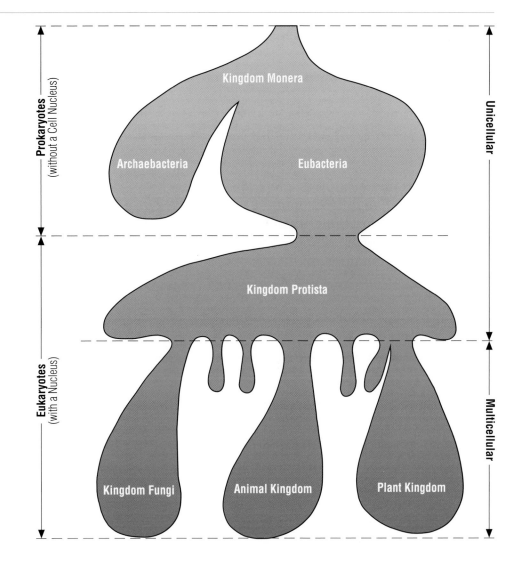

Fig 1.3
Animal Kingdom Diversity
After Barnes, Calow, & Olive, 1988

This diagram shows the relative proportion of different animal groups in terms of numbers of species. As indicated here, most animals on Earth are arthropods. This is due to the enormous number of insect species. In the sea, however, mollusks are the most diverse group.

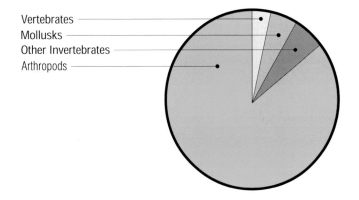

Invertebrates: A Quick Reference Guide is designed to give the reader a means of quickly identifying a large range of invertebrates. To accommodate scientific readers and casual readers of natural history, I include both common and Latin names where known, a practice standard in field guides even though the names in either case are subject to change. It is important to associate with each listing a region where the creature occurs in its natural habitat, to assist with the identification. This book features invertebrates mainly found in the tropics on or near coral reefs around the world, but the genera often include species whose range includes temperate or colder regions. Since the headings are on the level of genus, the range I list for each heading may extend beyond the bounds for individual species; such is the limitation of this quick reference style. To be more precise I sometimes offer additional range information for important species within the descriptions.

The descriptions also include information about color, size, special markings or other identifying features, and sometimes include details about the habitat where the creatures occur, or important associations with other creatures, such as commensals or parasites.

I try to use the simplest language possible in the descriptions, avoiding complex terms when a common word will suffice. Sometimes I even use incomplete sentences, for the sake of keeping the descriptions short. I apologize to readers who might prefer a more formal style of writing. Occasionally an uncommon term must be used within the descriptions, and in most cases the unfamiliar term can be found in the glossary.

Identifying some creatures can be complicated by the existence of look-alikes. For that reason the category "similar" offers a list of creatures that might be confused with the particular genus identified. In some instances the creatures listed in this category are not featured in this book. They can be found instead in some of the texts included in the suggested readings.

Aquarists need to know such things as temperature requirements, foods and feeding regimens, compatibility issues, and special husbandry requirements. The use of placement diagrams and charts regarding food, water motion, hardiness and aggressiveness made sense for providing quick reference husbandry information for a group of sessile animals such as corals. In the development of this book, however, I realized that the simple diagram style used in my book *Corals: A Quick Reference Guide* does not work well for all groups of invertebrates. In fact the best solution is to use text instead of diagrams, keeping this text to a minimum while providing the essential information. Thus I chose to give each heading some essential husbandry categories, and short descriptions to qualify them. The descriptions for the creatures offer information meant to compliment and enhance the quick reference subheadings, at the risk of occasionally being redundant. The headings include the following topics and the subheadings shown here offer the range of subjects covered by each heading.

Desirable/undesirable features:
  Ornamental.
  Useful in reef aquariums.
  Destructive or harmful to corals.
  Destructive to tridacnid clams.
  Destructive to worms.
  Toxic or harmful to people.
  Toxic or harmful to fishes.
  Toxic or harmful to invertebrates.
  Reef safe/not reef safe.

Food:
  Herbivorous.
  Carnivorous.
  Filter feeder.
  Detritivore.
  Photosynthetic.

Special considerations:
  Temperature
  Harmed by pump intakes or overflow drains.
  Harmed by fishes or other invertebrates.
  Aquarium size.
  Diet.

Hardiness in captivity:
  Hardy/not hardy or delicate to acclimate.
  Growth and reproduction.
  Life span - weeks - months - years.

The subheading "Reef safe/not reef safe" is subject to confusion because of the wide range of types of reef aquariums. By definition a reef aquarium features live rock, corals, and other reef animals and plants. Creatures I label as Reef Safe are generally not problematic in a typical reef aquarium, even if they may harm a particular type of coral or other invertebrate. Such exceptions are noted in the "Special considerations" or descriptions. Creatures that I label as not reef safe are either too destructive or unable to survive in a reef aquarium. They can be maintained in Fish aquariums or isolated in a species feature aquarium. The "Special considerations" in each case provides details about how the creature should be maintained.

Regarding hardiness in captivity, the subheading "Growth and reproduction" refers to the fact that the listed creature will grow and reproduce in aquariums, based on observations made by the author or personal communications with other aquarists. For hardy creatures that grow and reproduce, I just put "Growth and reproduction," omitting "Hardy." Some species do not reproduce in captivity despite the fact that they are hardy and easy to maintain. In such cases I state simply that they are hardy.

Some species naturally reproduce sexually and asexually (by vegetative division or budding). For these I do not always distinguish the mode of reproduction, only that they can multiply in aquaria, by whatever means. Further information can be found in the descriptions. Some species, giant clams for example, are cultivated for sale to aquarists. They can reproduce in aquariums, but are raised only under aquaculture conditions, not in the home aquarium.

The life span refers both to the life expectancy of the individual creature and to the length of time it can be maintained in aquaria. This subheading is a bit imprecise in some cases because there are creatures with a short life span that persist for years in aquaria by reproducing prolifically. An example of this trait is the acoel flatworm *Convolutriloba*, which reproduces by fission so that one individual divides rapidly into many. Combined with the subheading "Growth and reproduction," the fact that an individual may live only for weeks suggests that it can persist despite the short lifespan. I chose in this case and other similar ones to give the full range of life span to communicate the fact that the species persists while the individual does not.

Foraminiferans

Foraminiferans or "Forams" belong to the phylum Sarcodina, which includes the familiar amebas, among the simplest of protozoans. Members of this phylum produce finger-like flowing body extensions called pseudopodia (false feet) that are used for capturing food. In free-living species they are used for locomotion as well.

While amebas are quite simple in structure, the related Forams develop skeletons of fantastic complexity. Their skeletons are built on the framework of a secreted glycoprotein matrix, most commonly cemented together with secreted calcium carbonate to form a shell, but sometimes imbedded with gathered foreign mineral particles. This ability to secrete a skeleton also occurs in amebas. Shelled amebas are mostly freshwater or terrestrial (in damp soils and on moss) and their skeletons are made of chitin, silica, or an organic matrix with attached foreign mineral particles.

Foraminifera are primarily marine organisms. Most are benthic, a few are sessile, and there are also some planktonic species. Their pseudopodia are threadlike and composed of interconnected branches, known as reticulopodia.

The living foram fills the chambers of its shell, while its pseudopodia extend from the large opening of the shell. Sometimes a thin layer of cytoplasm that emerges from this shell opening covers the shell surface like a mantle, and the pseudopodia extend from it.

Foraminiferans feed on bacteria and organic matter trapped by the pseudopodia. Some may also trap protozoans or phytoplankton. A few benthic species are photosynthetic, possessing symbiotic algae. These special forms are common on the sun-exposed surfaces of shallow reefs, and on the blades of seagrasses.

A few types of forams are common, hardy aquarium inhabitants. Introduced with live rock and live sand or attached to live corals and clams, they grow and reproduce in aquaria. Seldom observed extremely minute species live in the sand. Some common photosynthetic species are really interesting and hardy, but are rarely found in aquariums because they are seldom harvested.

Homotrema

Common Name: Red Foram

Region: Circumtropical

Description: Red or pinkish small (usually not larger than 50mm individually) hard crusts or hard wart-like growths. Sometimes spiny, sometimes smooth. May cover the undersides of rocks or corals in groups spanning several centimetres. Their abundant skeletons make beach sands appear pinkish.

Similar: Often confused with coral, especially the Red Organpipe coral, *Tubipora*. Also confused with the hydrocoral *Stylaster* spp.

Desirable/undesirable features: Ornamental. Reef Safe.

Food: Filter feeder, organic matter, bacteria and microorganisms. Food additions not necessary.

Special considerations: Shade, water flow.

Hardiness in captivity: Growth and reproduction. Life span - years.

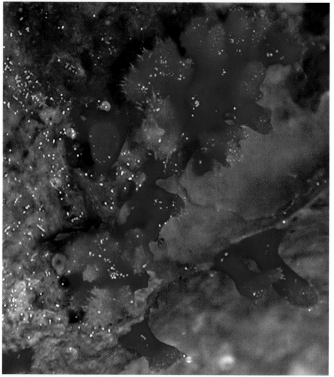

Homotrema rubrum, on the underside of a live rock. They proliferate in shade with strong water flow.

One can see the hair-like pseudopodia on this large *Homotrema rubrum*, Japan.

Marginopora

Common Name: Money Foram.

Region: Caribbean, Atlantic, Mediterranean, & Western Pacific.

Description: Disk shaped or washer shaped pale green or pink calcareous objects adhering to algae, seagrass, or hard substrates, including the shells of clams.

Similar: May be confused with coralline algae, bryozoans, or sand dollars.

Desirable/undesirable features: Ornamental. Reef Safe.

Food: Filter feeder, bacteria and microorganisms, photosynthetic.

Special considerations: Strong light, calcium and alkalinity for shell formation.

Hardiness in captivity: Growth and reproduction. Life span - months.

Marginopora is a coin-shaped foraminiferan common on reef slopes in the Western Pacific.

Marginopora are loosely attached to the live rock and may move. Solomon Islands.

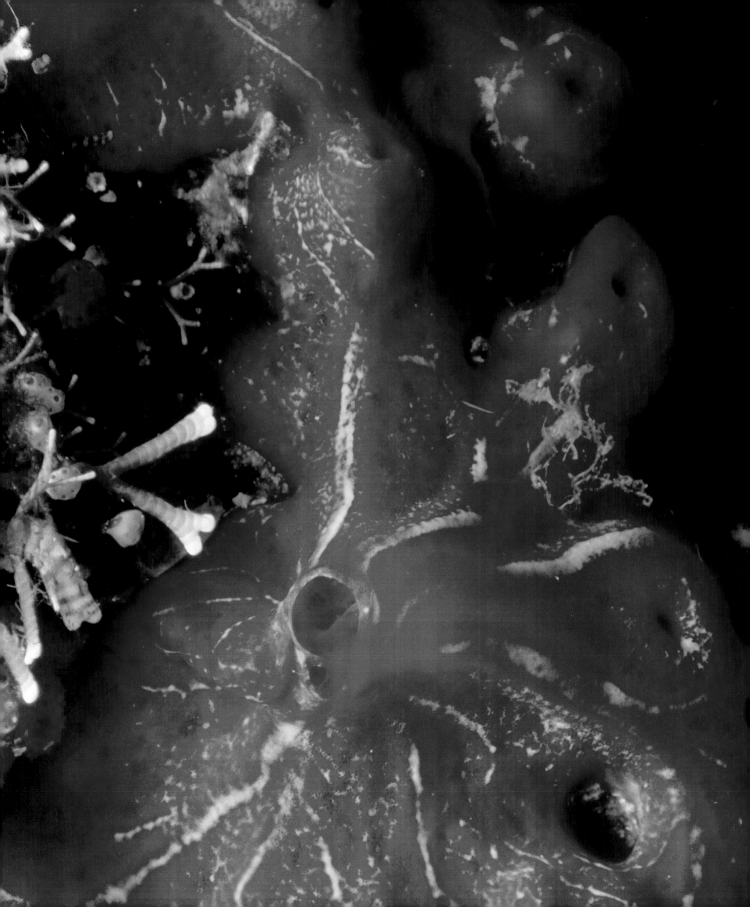

Sponges

Sponges are among the most primitive multicellular animals, but include a diverse variety of forms. They may be flat encrusting sheets, nets, fingers, branches, ribbons, vases, saucers, tubes, balls, pillows, or barrels. Some even live within and erode limestone rocks or the skeletons of living corals. The familiar sponge structure consists of proteinaceous fibers called spongin, but many sponges also include fiberglass-like siliceous or calcium carbonate structures called spicules. Some sponges build massive calcium carbonate skeletons that are coral-like, and capable of reef building.

The different plans of architecture are organized around a water transporting system of canals and chambers lined by special cells called choanocytes. Each choanocyte has a flagellum, a whip like structure that rotates to generate water currents. The beating flagella are the "pump" that transports water throughout the sponge. In addition, their shape and orientation to water flow in the environment provides another means of transporting water through the sponge. The ex-current apertures (called oscula because they look like little mouths) project their thin cone-shaped lips into the water stream passing over a sponge. The velocity of the current creates a pressure drop above these cones, causing water to flow out by Bernoulli's principle. Thus water currents provide a passive means of drawing water through the sponge. The effect allows greater opportunity to capture food and exchange respiratory gasses, at a reduced expenditure of energy. For this reason, many sponges proliferate in current swept localities, where they may grow to enormous sizes. Some sponges nevertheless proliferate in quiet water, relying only on their own pumping mechanism.

The food of sponges includes bacteria and phytoplankton, but the majority of what they consume is organic material much smaller in size, dissolved in the water. Choanocytes capture the extremely fine food in a mesh of tiny fingers that form a collar around each flagellum. Cells lining the in-current canals capture larger foods, and the sponge structure screens out very large particles. Some sponges contain symbiotic algae or cyanobacteria that supplement them with photosynthetically produced food. Many sponges utilize silicate to build spicules, but this element does not appear to be the limiting factor to growing most sponges. They are limited by food.

Not all sponges thrive in aquariums, but many do, and they provide colorful and interesting shapes that complete the appearance of a reef aquarium. In addition, they filter the water.

Chondrilla

Common Name: Chicken Liver Sponge

Region: Circumtropical and temperate seas including Mediterranean

Description: Rubbery encrusting sponge often with symbiotic algae. Usually brownish and mottled, but may be gray, black, dull orange, or brick-red.

Similar: Similar to various colonial tunicates.

Desirable/undesirable features: Ornamental. Reef safe. May encrust and kill corals. Bonds rocks together.

Food: Filter feeder, dissolved organic matter, bacteria. Photosynthetic. Food additions not necessary.

Special considerations: strong water flow, light.

Hardiness in captivity: Growth and reproduction. Life span - years.

Chicken Liver Sponge encrusting the roots of a Red mangrove. Key Biscayne, Florida.

Chondrilla nucula on live rock.   *Chondrilla nucula* on seagrass.

Dendrilla

Common Name: None

Region: Indonesia.

Description: Branchy with a mesh like structure that, combined with the light brown color, makes this sponge look like a soft coral.

Similar: None.

Desirable/undesirable features: Ornamental. Reef safe.

Food: Filter feeder, dissolved organic matter, bacteria. Photosynthetic?

Special considerations: strong water flow, food additions, light.

Hardiness in captivity: Poor. Life span - months.

Dendrilla is occasionally imported from Singapore and Indonesia. Kenny Tan, Singapore.

18

Collospongia

Common Name: Ear Sponge

Region: Indo-Pacific

Description: Blue, gray, purple or dark green laminar tiers or encrusting sheets with rubbery texture. Has symbiotic algae in tissue. Sometimes imported attached to live rock or with seaweeds. Captive propagation and trading among aquarists is the principal means of distribution of this species in the aquarium trade. May encrust shade and smother corals. Be careful to prevent this.

Similar: *Dysidea herbacea* and *Carteriospongia foliascens*.

Desirable/undesirable features: Ornamental. Reef safe. Harmful to corals.

Food: Filter feeder, dissolved organic matter, bacteria. Photosynthetic. Food additions not necessary.

Special considerations: Light.

Hardiness in captivity: Growth and reproduction. Life span - years.

Dysidea

Common Name: Conulose Sponge

Region: Circumtropical

Description: Encrusting or finger shaped sponge, with conulose or smooth surface. Soft or crisp texture, depending on species and water velocity conditions. Members of this genus are fed upon by several nudibranch species.

Similar: May be confused with *Ulosa, Aplysina, Aplysilla, Ircinia, Collospongia,* and other sponges.

Desirable/undesirable features: Ornamental. Reef safe.

Food: Filter feeder, organic matter, bacteria. Some species are Photosynthetic.

Special considerations: Light for photosynthetic species.

Hardiness in captivity: *Dysidea herbacea* is hardy. *Dysidea etheria* is not as hardy but grows well when given dissolved organic food. Life span - months - years.

Collospongia auris has symbiotic algae and thrives in brightly illuminated aquariums.

Collospongia auris can smother corals. It should be trimmed often to keep it from growing over them.

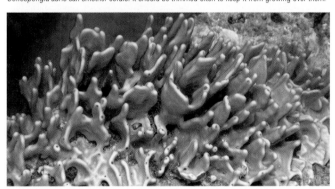
Dysidea herbacea is photosynthetic, hardy, and long-lived in brightly illuminated aquariums.Fiji.

Dysidea etheria from Florida.

This nudibranch feeds on *Dysidea fragilis*.

19

Aplysina

Common Name: Yellow Tube Sponge, Yellow Finger Sponge.

Region: Circumtropical and in the Mediterranean.

Description: Finger or tube-shaped sponge, with conulose or smooth surface. Soft or crisp texture, depending on species and water velocity conditions. Most are yellow. *Aplysina cauliformis* and some other species have violet pigment. Color changes with exposure to air (yellow species turn green).

Similar: May be confused with *Ircinia*, *Verongia*, and other sponges.

Desirable/undesirable features: Ornamental. Reef safe.

Food: Filter feeder, dissolved organic matter, bacteria. Photosynthetic.

Special considerations: Light. Strong water motion. Do not expose to air.

Hardiness in captivity: Hardy. Life span - months - years.

Aplysina fistularis. Key Biscayne, Florida.

Ircinia

Common Name: Stinking Sponge.

Region: Circumtropical.

Description: Lobe shaped, branching, vase shaped, or massive sponges with thick rubbery tissue. Usually gray or black.

Similar: May be confused with *Aplysina*, *Dysidea*, *Carteriospongia* and other sponges.

Desirable/undesirable features: Ornamental. Reef safe.

Food: Filter feeder, dissolved organic matter, bacteria. Photosynthetic.

Special considerations: Light. Strong water motion.

Hardiness in captivity: Hardy. Life span - months - years.

A lobe-shaped *Ircinia* sp. from Florida.

Ianthella

Common Name: Saucer Sponge, Elephant Ear Sponge

Region: Indian Ocean and Western Pacific.

Description: Large Ear shaped or vase shaped sponges with flexible rubbery tissue. Usually yellow, green, or purple. Commonly with commensal sea cucumbers and gobies on its surface.

Similar: Small speciments may be confused with *Dysidea, Phyllospongia, Carteriospongia* and other sponges.

Desirable/undesirable features: Ornamental. Reef safe.

Food: Filter feeder, dissolved organic matter, bacteria. Photosynthetic.

Special considerations: Light. Strong water motion. Daily supplemental feeding.

Hardiness in captivity: Not very hardy.
Life span - months - years.

Ianthella basta. Solomon Islands.

Ianthella basta often has commensal sea cucumbers on its surface. Solomon Islands.

Pseudosuberites

Common Name: Yellow ball sponge

Region: Indo Pacific

Description: Dull to bright yellow lumpy sponge with distinct oscula and thick velvety surface.

Similar: *Aplysina*

Desirable/undesirable features: Reef safe.

Food: Filter feeder, dissolved organic matter, bacteria.

Special considerations: Strong water flow.

Hardiness in captivity: Hardy.
Life span - years.

Pseudosuberites from Singapore, Kenny Tan.

21

Cynachyra and *Cynachyrella*

Common Name: Ball Sponge, Moon Sponge

Region: Indo-Pacific, Caribbean, Mediterranean

Description: Ball shaped sponges up to 12 inches (30 cm) in diameter, but typically only about 2 inches (5 cm). The oscula are large and look like craters on the sponge surface, giving a moon-like appearance. Commonly yellow, but may be brown or pink. Has a very stiff consistency due to dense siliceous skeletal fibers. Surface may be coated with detritus or algae, hiding the sponge's true appearance.

Similar: *Tethya* spp., which are softer and don't have the recessed crater-like oscula.

Desirable/undesirable features: Ornamental. Reef safe.

Food: Filter feeder, dissolved organic matter, bacteria.

Special considerations: None.

Hardiness in captivity: Very hardy. Life span - years.

Cinachyrella sp. Solomon Islands.

Cinachyra alloclada from Florida is hardy and long-lived in aquariums.

22

Tethya

Common Name: Ball sponge

Region: Indo-Pacific, Caribbean, Mediterranean

Description: Small ball shaped sponge, usually not more than 3 inches (7.6 cm) in diameter, colored yellow, orange, green, or red. The surface is smooth or bumpy. Sponge is firm but softer than *Cynachyra* and *Cynachyrella*. This sponge reproduces by budding off hundreds of tiny individuals. Some species "walk" by means of extended hair-like appendages that attach to adjacent substrate.

Similar: *Cinachyra* and *Cynachyrella*.

Desirable/undesirable features: Ornamental. Reef safe.

Food: Filter feeder, dissolved organic matter, bacteria.

Special considerations: Some species prefer strong water motion.

Hardiness in captivity: Growth and reproduction. Life span - years.

A reef-dwelling *Tethya* sp. from Florida.

Tethya sp. from a seagrass bed, showing numerous budded offspring still attached.

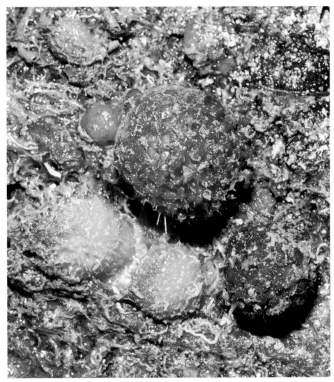

Two species of *Tethya* in three colors on the underside of a rock, Biscayne Bay, Florida.

Teichaxinella

Common Name: Ruffled Sponge

Region: Circumtropical

Description: Yellow or orange flabellate sponge of about the size of a fist or smaller, with a texture like soft velvet. Usually attached by a central stalk.

Similar: May be confused with *Stylissa*, which is much stiffer, and not velvety.

Desirable/undesirable features: Oranamental. Reef safe.

Food: Filter feeder, dissolved organic matter, bacteria. Requires supplemental feeding of dissolved organic food to thrive.

Special considerations: Strong water flow. Food additions.

Hardiness in captivity: The yellow soft species is hardy. The orange stiff species is not. Life span - months-years.

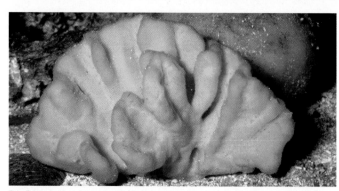

This *Teichaxinella* sp. is easy to maintain in aquariums. It occurs in the Caribbean and West Pacific.

Teichaxinella? sp., Cactus Sponge from Singapore. Kenny Tan. It does not live long in aquariums.

Acanthella

Common Name: Spiny Sponge

Region: Singapore, Indonesia, Western Pacific.

Description: Highly perforated red, orange or yellow upright ball-shaped or irregular masses arising from a single trunk-like base.

Similar: *Dendrilla, Teichaxinella, Stylissa.*

Desirable/undesirable features: Ornamental. Reef safe.

Food: Filter feeder, dissolved organic matter, bacteria. Requires daily supplemental feeding of dissolved organic food to thrive.

Special considerations: Strong water flow. Food additions.

Hardiness in captivity: Not very hardy.
Life span - months-years.

Acanthella sp. from Singapore. Kenny Tan.

Pseudaxinella

Common Name: Red Ball Sponge.

Region: Caribbean.

Description: Thick orange sponge of about the same size and shape as a fist. Occasionally much larger.

Similar: Small specimens may be confused with *Tethya*.

Desirable/undesirable features: Reef safe. Damaged specimens may release toxic mucus that may harm fish.

Food: Filter feeder, dissolved organic matter, bacteria. Requires supplemental feeding of dissolved organic food to thrive.

Special considerations: Strong water flow. Food additions.

Hardiness in captivity: Fairly hardy.
Life span- months -years.

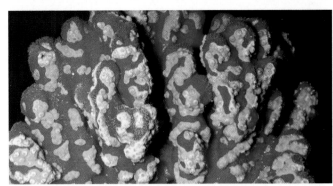

Pseudaxinella lunaecharta with commensal *Parazoanthus* sp. on its surface.

Three small *Pseudaxinella lunaecharta.* Exotic Aquariums, Miami, Florida.

Axinella

Common Name: Finger Sponge.

Region: Circumtropical and in some temperate regions.

Description: Red, orange or yellow upright branches from a single trunk-like base. Branches smooth with many small oscula all over the surface and a velvety texture.

Similar: *Ptilocaulis* and *Auletta.*

Desirable/undesirable features: Ornamental. Reef safe.

Food: Filter feeder, dissolved organic matter, bacteria. Requires daily supplemental feeding of dissolved organic food to thrive.

Special considerations: Strong water flow. Food additions.

Hardiness in captivity: Not very hardy.
Life span - months - years.

Axinella sp. planted naturally in an aquarium with strong water flow.

Higginsia and *Ptilocaulis*

Common Name: Red Finger Sponge, Tree Sponge.

Region: Florida, Caribbean.

Description: Red, Orange, or yellow upright branching, tree-shaped or bushy, with a single trunk-like base. Firm but flexible. Sometimes forming long rope-like fingers. Surface of fingers has rough conulose texture, somewhat like branchy *Acropora* spp. corals.

Similar: *Axinella* and *Teichaxinella* spp. The genus *Ptilocaulis* includes species in the Caribbean and Indo-Pacific that are superficially identical to *Higginsia strigillata*. *Amphimedon compressa* has a smoother surface with larger, more obvious randomly scattered oscula.

Desirable/undesirable features: Ornamental. Reef safe.

Food: Filter feeder, dissolved organic matter, bacteria. Requires supplemental feeding of dissolved organic food to thrive.

Special considerations: Strong water flow. Food additions.

Hardiness in captivity: Poor.
Life span - months - years (with care).

Smooth textured *Ptilocaulis* sp. from Florida.

Yellow *Ptilocaulis* sp. from Florida with very rough surface texture.

Rough textured *Ptilocaulis* sp. from Florida.

Auletta

Common Name: Yellow Finger Sponge

Region: Western Pacific

Description: Bright yellow or orange yellow upright branches originating from a common base. Prominent oscula at branch ends.

Similar: *Axinella*

Desirable/undesirable features: Ornamental. Reef safe.

Food: Filter feeder, dissolved organic matter, bacteria. Requires supplemental feeding of dissolved organic food to thrive.

Special considerations: Strong water flow. Food additions.

Hardiness in captivity: Poor.
Life span - months - years (with care).

Auletta sp. Solomon Islands.

Clathria

Common Name: Paddle Sponge, Vase Sponge

Region: Circumtropical

Description: Flabellate, palmate (usually), digitate, or massive red or orange sponge arising from a short cylindrical stalk by which it attaches to the substrate. *Clathria rugosa* is a common import from Indonesia. Other species of *Clathria* are low encrusting sponges with prominent canals in star patterns around the oscula, much like *Monanchora* spp. The author believes the paddle-shaped sponge described here belongs to a different genus, close to *Axinella*.

Similar: *Axinella* and *Pseudaxinella*

Desirable/undesirable features: Reef safe.

Food: Filter feeder, dissolved organic matter, bacteria. Requires supplemental feeding of dissolved organic food to thrive.

Special considerations: Strong water flow. Food additions.

Hardiness in captivity: Poor.
Life span - months - years (with care).

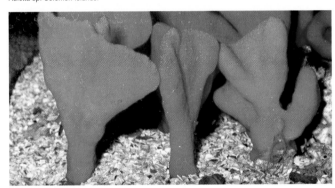

Clathria rugosa? from Indonesia.

Clathria rugosa? from Indonesia. Aquarium Center, Randallstown, Maryland.

Stylissa

Common Name: Cork Sponge

Region: Circumtropical?

Description: Foliaceous or flabellate, bumpy stiff and often flattened in one plane, attached to substrate by a small basal stalk. Usually orange, sometimes brown or yellow.

Similar: *Axinella carteri*, *Teichaxinella* spp.

Desirable/undesirable features: Reef safe.

Food: Filter feeder, organic matter, bacteria. Requires supplemental feeding of dissolved organic food to thrive.

Special considerations: Strong water flow. Food additions. Algae may attach to the spiny surface and smother this sponge.

Hardiness in captivity: Poor.
Life span - months - years (with care).

Stylissa carteri, the Cactus Sponge from Indonesia.

Gelloides

Common Name: Cactus Sponge

Region: Western Pacific

Description: *Gelloides fibulata* forms thin brittle branches with tapered blunt or pointed tips. Surface and the tips of branches are very spiky. The spikes are sharp and stiff, hence the common name.

Similar: *Niphates*, to which it is closely related.

Desirable/undesirable features: Ornamental. Reef safe.

Food: Filter feeder, dissolved organic matter, bacteria. Supplemental feeding of dissolved organic food improves growth.

Special considerations: Strong water flow.

Hardiness in captivity: Hardy. Life span - months - years.

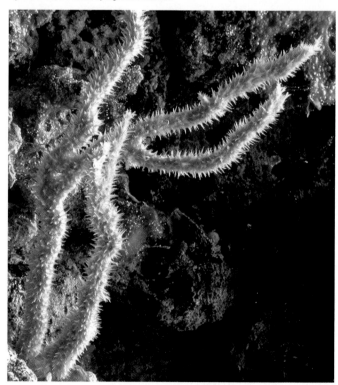
Gelloides fibulata, the Cactus Sponge from Singapore. Kenny Tan.

Niphates

Common Name: Finger Sponge

Region: Circumtropical

Description: Brittle branches with tapered blunt or pointed tips. Also some vase shaped species with spiky rims. Surface may be smooth or papillated and the tips of branches are often spiky. Not commercially harvested. The common pinkish species in South Florida is a worthwhile sponge for aquariums.

Similar: *Haliclona* forms similar crisp fingers with a smoother surface texture. *Calyspongia* forms vase shapes with surface texture much like *Niphates*.

Desirable/undesirable features: Ornamental. Reef safe.

Food: Filter feeder, dissolved organic matter, bacteria. Supplemental feeding of dissolved organic food improves growth.

Special considerations: Strong water flow.

Hardiness in captivity: Growth and reproduction.
Life span - months - years.

Niphates sp. on a seagrass bed with strong tidal currents in Florida.

Niphates erecta from Florida is both beautiful and hardy. Key Biscayne, Florida.

Callyspongia

Common Name: Vase Sponge, Tube Sponge

Region: Circumtropical

Description: Most *Callyspongia* are vase or tube shaped, with crisp texture and irregular surface. Often shades of purple. *Callyspongia plicifera* in the Caribbean has startling blue and purple color. Some species are twig like. *Callyspongia subarmigera* forms greenish or brown string-like branches and proliferates in aquariums in bright light. This genus is short lived in nature and in aquariums.

Similar: *Niphates*.

Desirable/undesirable features: Ornamental. Reef safe.

Food: Filter feeder, dissolved organic matter, bacteria. Photosynthetic. Requires supplemental feeding of dissolved organic food to thrive.

Special considerations: Strong water flow. Food additions. Light.

Hardiness in captivity: Poor.
Life span - months.

The fluorescent Azure Vase Sponge, *Callyspongia plicifera* is lovely but short lived in aquariums.

29

Haliclona

Common Name: Finger Sponge, Blue Sponge

Region: Pacific, Indian, Red Sea, Caribbean

Description: Brightly colored (blue, purple, green) soft to firm fingers with several prominent oscula on each branch. Branch tips are rounded. Lives in full sunlight in shallow water.

Similar: *Amphimedon. Sigmadocia* and *Adocia*. Nilsen and Fosså report a species of *Xestospongia* that is superficially like the blue *Haliclona* sp. from Indonesia.

Desirable/undesirable features: Reef safe. Except *Amphimedon compressa*, which is toxic to fishes.

Food: Filter feeder, dissolved organic matter, bacteria. Photosynthetic.

Special considerations: Strong water flow. Light.

Hardiness in captivity: Growth and reproduction. Life span - months - years (with care).

Purple *Adocia* sp. growing in David Saxby's aquarium, London, England.

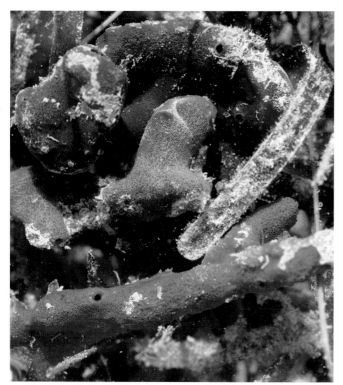

Two color morphs of the Caribbean sponge *Amphimedon* (=*Haliclona*) *viridis*.

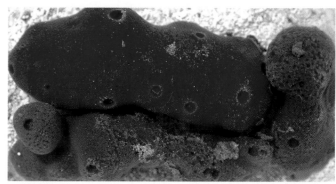

The red sponge, *A. compressa,* is very toxic to fish! The green sponge, *A. viridis* is safe. Florida.

Sigmadocia? sp. on a seagrass bed in strong light.

Sigmadocia? sp. from Florida.

Haliclona or *Kallypilidion* sp. from Singapore, Kenny Tan.

Blue *Haliclona* sp. from Indonesia, photographed in the aquarium of David Saxby, London, England.

Haliclona molitba, a hardy and brightly colored species that lives in full sunshine.

31

Agelas

Common Name: Orange Elephant Ear Sponge

Region: Circumtropical

Description: Thick stiff massive, branching or tube-shaped sponge with many short deep channels on surface. Typically yellow, brownish red, or orange.

Similar: *Didiscus, Placospongia, Myrmekioderma*

Desirable/undesirable features: Reef safe. Avoid large specimens, which may harm aquarium if they die and foul the water.

Food: Filter feeder, organic matter, bacteria. Requires supplemental feeding of dissolved organic food to thrive.

Special considerations: Strong water flow. Food additions.

Hardiness in captivity: Poor.
Life span - months - years (with care).

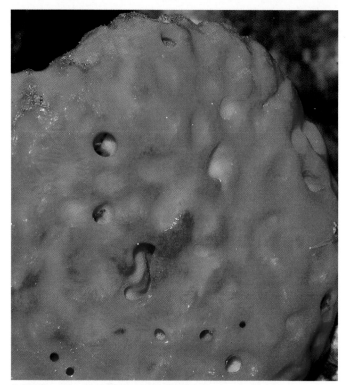

Agelas clathrodes from Florida. Country Critters, New York.

Placospongia

Common Name: Wood Sponge, Alligator Sponge

Region: Circumtropical

Description: Thick stiff massive, encrusting or branching sponge with many long deep channels (containing the ostia and oscula) on a hard surface that appears to be divided into plates. Typically brownish red, or dull orange, and often covered with fine calcium carbonate dust. Very hardy in aquariums.

Similar: *Didiscus, Agelas. Myrmekioderma*

Desirable/undesirable features: Reef safe.

Food: Filter feeder, dissolved organic matter, bacteria. Does not require supplemental feeding.

Special considerations: Strong water flow.

Hardiness in captivity: Growth and reproduction.
Life span - years.

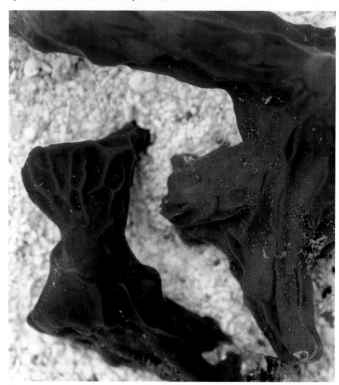

Placospongia is a hardy sponge with a wood-like appearance.

Sycon

Common Name: Urn Sponge

Region: Ubiquitous

Description: Small urn-shaped sponges. Commonly introduced to aquariums with live rock.

Similar: May be confused with tunicates. *Leucaltis* forms larger growths of connected tubes with similar overall appearance to *Sycon*.

Desirable/undesirable features: Reef safe.

Food: Filter feeder, dissolved organic matter, bacteria. Does not require supplemental feeding.

Special considerations: None.

Hardiness in captivity: Growth and reproduction. Life span - years.

Sycon proliferates in aquariums on live rock, under corals, in filters, pipes, and other shady zones.

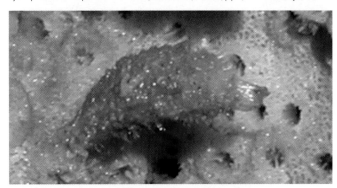

Sycon on the undersides of a coral. Note the dense hair-like siliceous spicules

Clathrina

Common Name: Leather Latticework Sponge

Region: Circumtropical, and Mediterranean.

Description: Colonies composed of a network or mesh-like lattice of tubes. Often inconspicuous small encrustations on undersides of rocks or overhangs. Sometimes forming thick masses up to the size of a grapefruit. Commonly introduced to aquariums with live rock.

Similar: Several algae resemble *Clathrina*, including the brown alga *Hydroclathrus* and a dark brown colored red alga.

Desirable/undesirable features: Reef safe.

Food: Filter feeder, dissolved organic matter, bacteria. Does not require supplemental feeding.

Special considerations: Strong water flow. Does not like bright light.

Hardiness in captivity: Growth and reproduction. Life span - years.

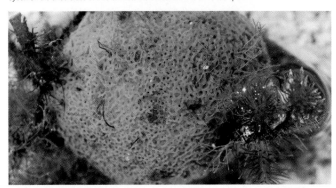

Bright yellow *Clathrina coriacea* commonly proliferates in aquariums in shady zones.

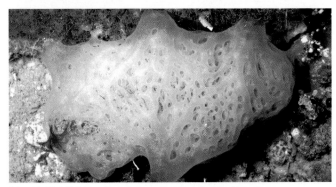

This unidentified *Clathrina* sp. forms large masses on the undersides of live rock.

Cnidaria

The phylum Cnidaria includes stony and soft corals, corallimorphs, anemones, zoanthids, cerianthids, black corals hydroids, fire corals, siphonophores, and jellyfish. The ctenophores or comb jellies (phylum Ctenophora) once were considered members of the Cnidaria, but are now classified as a separate phylum. I include them here with the Cnidaria as a matter of convenience, common practice in some texts that group the two phyla together as "coelenterates." While the first book in the Oceanographic Series, *Corals: A Quick Reference Guide* covers hard and soft corals, and fire corals, this chapter describes species from the above-mentioned group (except siphonophores) that are commonly maintained in aquariums.

Corallimorphs and anemones form solitary polyps and colonies of clones, much like the stony corals to which they are closely related. Corallimorphs are often confused with true sea anemones and with corals. Cerianthids are anemone-like cnidarians with an anal pore, and they build a flexible tube partially buried in soft sediments.

Zoanthids form clusters of polyps and encrusting mats that are often called false corals or erroneously, soft corals or colonial anemones. Like corals and anemones, some zoanthids have symbiotic zooxanthellae. Some incorporate sand grains in their tissues, making them feel like slimy sandpaper. Others are commensals living in association with sponges, hydroids, hermit crabs, or polychaete worms.

Black corals form whip, coil, bottlebrush, fan and tree-like growths composed of a tough horn-like material. Their tentacles extend in rows from the branches and catch zooplankton.

Hydroids usually form feathery colonies with tiny polyps, or encrusting root-like colonies with larger upright polyps. Many have a powerful sting. Some harbor symbiotic algae. For part of their life cycle they form free-swimming medusae that look like small jellyfish.

Jellyfish, and ctenophores are distinct gelatinous animals. Most jellyfish form bell-shaped medusae, and for part of their life cycle they form attached polyps. Some jellyfish are always attached, never free-swimming, and a few remain near the bottom though they can swim.

Ctenophores are mostly planktonic creatures about the size and shape of a kiwi fruit or grape, bearing rows of beating "combs." Some species are wing-shaped. A few benthic species are ameba-shaped, and they are commonly introduced to aquariums with the seastars, soft corals, or seaweeds on which they cling.

Aglaophenia

Common Name: Stinging Hydroid

Region: Western Pacific

Description: Tall (to at least 60 cm) sturdy fern-shaped colonies with golden brown color from symbiotic algae. While it has a powerful sting that is painful to humans, leaving a rash that lasts for days, the effects on fishes are unknown. It may be easy to maintain in a brightly illuminated aquarium with strong water flow. It should not be harvested for home aquariums because of the danger of its powerful sting, but it could make an interesting public aquarium exhibit.

Similar: *Lytocarpus* spp. Several smaller non-photosynthetic Hydroids that feed on zooplankton have fern-like shapes, and a few species of red algae may have the same growth form.

Desireable/undesireable features: Ornamental. Toxic to people. Harmful to fishes? Reef safe?

Food: Filter feeder, zooplankton. Photosynthetic

Special considerations: Strong water flow. Light.

Hardiness in captivity: Unknown.

Aglaophenia cupressina with cardinal fishes, Solomon Islands.

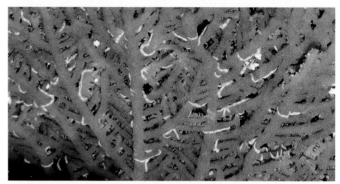

Aglaophenia cupressina with commensal brittle stars, Solomon Islands.

Solanderia

Common Name: Sea Fan

Region: Circumtropical

Description: Very gorgonian-like, with horny axis and often with colorful tissue (purple or yellow). Sting is mild. They feed on zooplankton on current swept reef walls.

Similar: Gorgonians and Sea Fans

Desireable/undesireable features: Ornamental. Reef safe.

Food: Filter feeder, zooplankton.

Special considerations: Strong water flow. Supplemental food.

Hardiness in captivity: Unknown

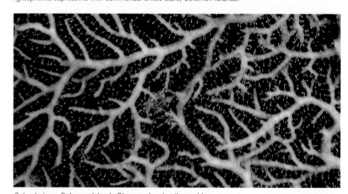

Solanderia sp. Solomon Islands.Closeup showing the zooids.

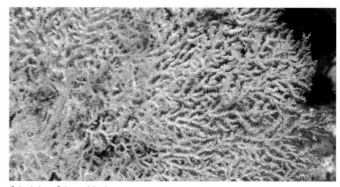

Solanderia sp. Solomon Islands.

Myrionema

Common Name: Stinging Hydroid

Region: Western Pacific

Description: Very soft coral-like, with a creeping stolon and brown feathery polyps. Sting is mild. Fast growing in strong light, and dependent on the photosynthetic products of its symbiotic algae. The sting is damaging to neighboring corals. This species is a pest in reef aquariums. It can be controlled with nudibranchs that feed on hydroids (there are many) such as *Pteraeolidia ianthina*. Keyhole limpets sometimes feed on *Myrionema* and are another possible control.

Similar: Stoloniferous soft corals.

Desireable/undesireable features: Harmful to corals and tridacnid clams. Not reef safe.

Food: Filter feeder, photosynthetic

Special considerations: Light

Hardiness in captivity: Growth and reproduction. Life span - years.

Myrionema growing on a branchy sponge in an aquarium in the UK.

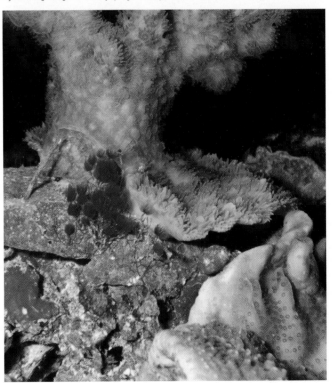

The photosynthetic hydroid *Myrionema* stings stony corals.

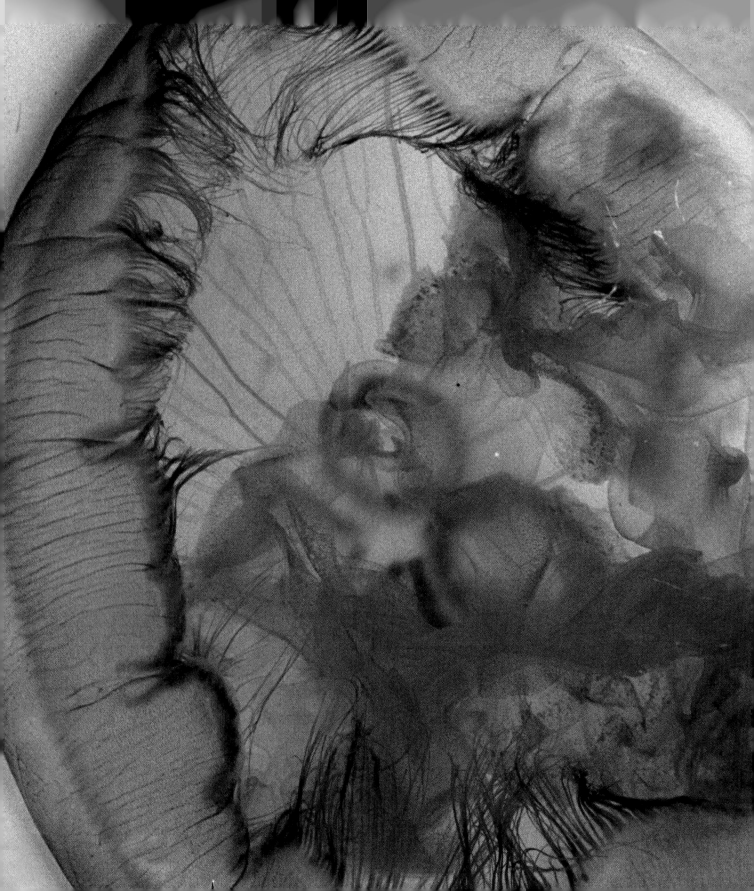

Nausithoe and *Stephanoscyphus*

Common Name: Hydroid, Tubular Sponge Polyp

Region: Circumtropical

Description: Often mistaken for hydroids or zoanthids, these small polyps are common on live rock and sponges. They are the polyp stage of a coronate jellyfish, and some have symbiotic zooxanthellae. Their ephyrae (larval medusae) are sometimes seen in reef aquariums. *Stephanoscyphus* spp. have a very powerful sting! Do not touch them.

Similar: The polyp stage of other jellyfishes may resemble these, and small zoanthids bear remarkable resemblance to large polyps of *Stephanoscyphus*.

Desireable/undesireable features: Reef safe. Toxic to people.

Food: Filter feeder, photosynthetic.

Special considerations: Illumination for zooxanthellate spp.

Hardiness in captivity: Growth and reproduction. Life span - years.

These small polyps look like zoanthids but are the jellyfish, *Stephanocyphus*. David Saxby's aquarium.

Stephanoscyphus, Japan. *Nausithoe* sp. Fiji.

Linuche

Common Name: Thimble Jellyfish

Region: Indo-Pacific, Caribbean

Description: Small, thimble-shaped (and sized) jellyfish usually dark brown due to dense populations of symbiotic zooxanthellae. Often occurs in large swarms in the open ocean in clear water. Sometimes nearshore in the vicinity of reefs. Not presently harvested, but the author believes this jellyfish could be a popular species for special small jellyfish aquariums.

Similar: None.

Desireable/undesireable features: Not reef safe. Toxic to people.

Food: Filter feeder, photosynthetic.

Special considerations: Strong illumination required. Harmed by pump intakes or overflow drains. May require supplemental feeding of zooplankton (or *Artemia* nauplii).

Hardiness in captivity: Growth and reproduction. Life span - years.

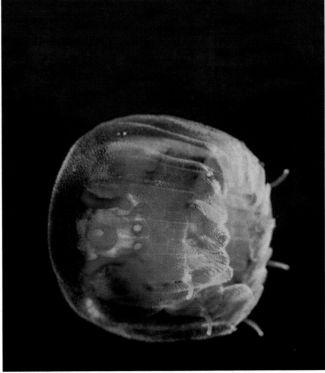

Linuche unguiculata has symbiotic zooxanthellae and may thus be easy to maintain. Paul Humann.

Cassiopeia

Common Name: Upside-down Jellyfish

Region: Circumtropical

Description: The bell is flattened into a disc that is usually top down on a sandy or muddy substrate in calm shallow bays. Highly branched oral arms resemble fleshy macroalgae that are common in the habitat where they occur. This jellyfish has symbiotic zooxanthellae, but also has powerful nematocysts for catching zooplankton prey. Usually brown with white and gray markings, but sometimes very colorful, with blue, violet, and green pigment.

Similar: There are several species. *Mastigias* and *Phyllorhiza* are similar but have rounded bells.

Desireable/undesireable features: Not reef safe. Toxic to people.

Food: Filter feeder, photosynthetic.

Special considerations: Strong illumination required. Harmed by pump intakes or overflow drains. May require daily supplemental feeding of zooplankton (or *Artemia* nauplii) if not strongly illuminated.

Hardiness in captivity: Growth and reproduction. Life span - years.

Cassiopea xamachana, the common Upside-down Jellyfish, Florida Keys.

Cassiopea sp. Eilat, Israel.

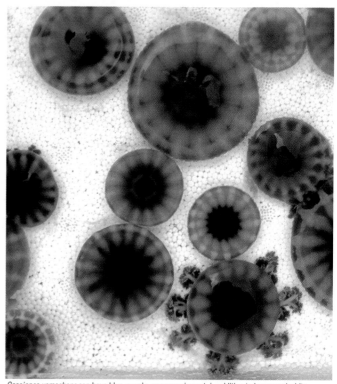

Cassiopea xamachana can have blue, purple, or green pigment, in addition to brown and white.

Mastigias

Common Name:

Region: Indo-Pacific, Caribbean (introduced)

Description: Rounded bell with a scalloped margin and highly branched but compact tentacles. *Mastigias papua* has whitish polka-dots. There may be other species without these markings. Has symiotic zooxanthellae. Occurs in lagoons or bays in shallow water, usually near the bottom. A small relative of this jellyfish is occasionally harvested in the Philippines. It commonly is brown, green, or blue.

Similar: *Phyllorhiza punctata*

Desireable/undesireable features: Not reef safe.

Food: Filter feeder, photosynthetic.

Special considerations: Strong illumination beneficial. Harmed by pump intakes or overflow drains. Requires daily supplemental feeding of zooplankton (or *Artemia* nauplii).

Hardiness in captivity: Growth and reproduction. Life span - years.

Mastigias papua has large white spots on its bell. Solomon Islands.

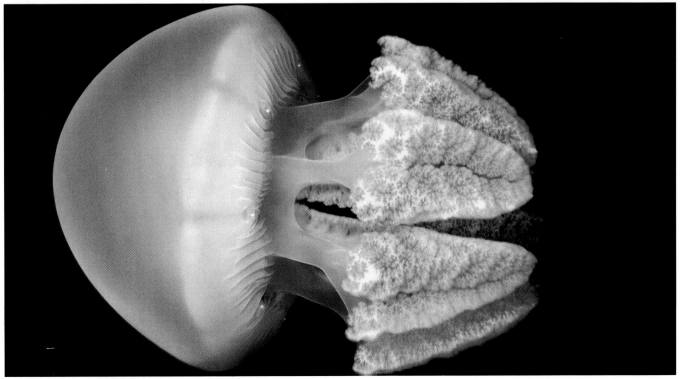

Mastigias or *Phyllorhiza* sp. at the Osaka Aquarium, Japan.

41

Aurelia

Common Name: Moon Jellyfish

Region: All oceans, from the tropics into sub-arctic regions.

Description: Bell diameter to more than 14 inches, with a clover-shaped mark (the gonads) in the center. Commonly displayed in public aquaria. Captive culture programs rear large numbers. Captive specimens are nearly colorless. Wild specimens often have pigments in the bell, pink gonads, and purple tentacles, a product of the food the jellyfish consumes.

Similar: Not likely to be confused with other jellyfish.

Desireable/undesireable features: Not reef safe. Toxic to people.

Food: Filter feeder. Zooplankton.

Special considerations: Harmed by pump intakes or drains. Requires daily supplemental feeding of zooplankton (or *Artemia* nauplii). Some species require chilled water.

Hardiness in captivity: Growth and reproduction.
Life span - years.

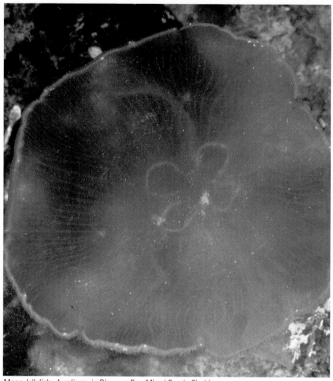

Moon Jellyfish, *Aurelia* sp. in Biscayne Bay, Miami Beach, Florida.

The larvae of *Aurelia aurita* in a culture tank at the Monterey Bay Aquarium.

This *Aurelia* sp. washed up on the beach on Virginia Key, Florida has pink gonads.

Chrysaora

Common Name: Sea Nettle

Region: Japan, Bering Sea, Alaska to California

Description: *Chrysaora fuscescens* is orange-brown while *C. melanaster* has a pattern of stripes on the bell. Both have long, folded oral arms and very elongate tentacles. Maintained in special Kreisel aquariums at a few public aquariums, such as the Monterey Bay Aquarium, Long Beach Aquarium, and Osaka Aquarium. They are mesmerizing!

Similar: None

Desireable/undesireable features: Not reef safe. Toxic to people.

Food: Filter feeder. Zooplankton.

Special considerations: Harmed by pump intakes or overflow drains. Requires daily supplemental feeding of zooplankton (or *Artemia* nauplii). Chilled water.

Hardiness in captivity: Growth and reproduction. Life span - years.

A spectacular exhibit of *Chrysaora melanaster* at the Osaka Aquarium, Japan.

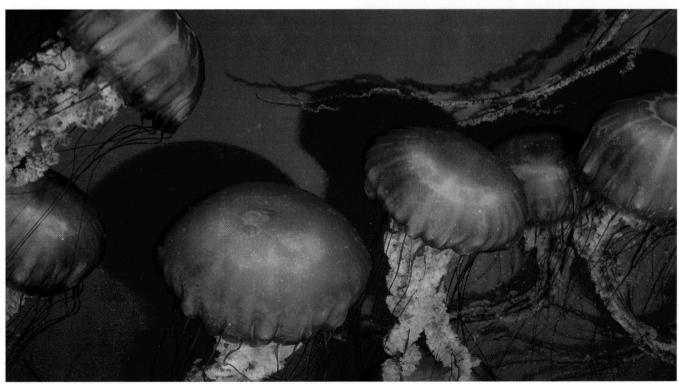

Chrysaora fuscescens at the Monterey Bay Aquarium. Observing this display is among the best public aquarium experiences.

Palythoa

Common Name: False Coral, Colonial Anemones

Region: Circumtropical

Description: Anemone-like polyps imbedded in a common tissue (coenenchyme) that is slimy but with a sand-paper-like texture due to entrapped sand grains. Color is light brown due to symbiotic zooxanthellae, but *Palythoa* spp. readily feed on all kinds of meaty foods. These colonies encrust corals and rocks, sometimes overgrowing and killing stony corals in reef areas affected by high or low temperatures or high nutrient levels, which *Palythoa* tolerates better than most stony corals.

Similar: *Protopalythoa*. There are species with characteristics of both that really link the two genera. *Palythoa* spp. superficially resemble faviid stony corals.

Desireable/undesireable features: Ornamental. Harmful to corals. Toxic to people. Reef safe.

Food: Carnivorous, filter feeder, photosynthetic.

Special considerations: Light. *Palythoa* is toxic to most corals and is also toxic to humans. Contact with the mucus can produce severe rash or allergic reactions.

Hardiness in captivity: Growth and reproduction.
Life span - years.

Palythoa tuberculosa is intermediate between *Palythoa* and *Protopalythoa*. Florida Keys.

Palythoa caribbaeorum from Florida slowly grows over and kills stony corals.

Palythoa caesia with a "fire coral," *Millepora*, common neighbors. Solomon Islands.

Protopalythoa

Common Name: Button Polyps, Zoanthids, False Coral, Colonial Anemones

Region: Circumtropical and some temperate regions

Description: Colonies consisting of clusters of separate anemone-like polyps connected at their point of attachment with the substrate, but not imbedded in a common tissue. Tentacles are pointed at tips and usually alternate up-down-up-down. Slimy but with a sand-paper-like texture due to entrapped sand grains. Color brown, often with fluorescent green, or orange pigment. *Protopalythoa* spp. have symbiotic zooxanthellae but feed on all kinds of meaty foods.

Similar: *Palythoa.* There are species with characteristics of both that really link the two genera. *Zoanthus* spp. are not usually slimy, don't trap sand grains, and have blunter tentacles.

Desireable/undesireable features: Ornamental. Harmful to corals. Toxic to people. Reef safe.

Food: Carnivorous, filter feeder, photosynthetic.

Special considerations: Light. *Protopalythoa* is toxic to most stony corals and is also toxic to humans. Contact with the mucus can produce severe rash or allergic reactions.

Hardiness in captivity: Growth and reproduction. Life span - years.

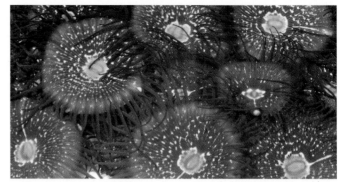

A typical color scheme of *Protopalythoa* spp., Japan.

Protopalythoa sp. from Singapore, Kenny Tan.

Protopalythoa spp. often have fluorescent green centers on their oral discs. Kenny Tan.

Protopalythoa psammophila. Hawai'i.

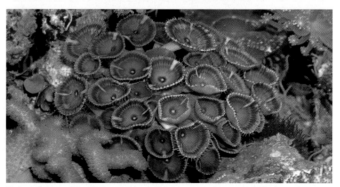

Protopalythoa grandis has the largest polyps of the genus, spanning more than 2 inches each.

Isaurus

Common Name: Snake Polyps

Region: Circumtropical and in some temperate regions.

Description: Polyps are elongate and bend toward the substrate. Tentacles expand at night only, and actively catch zooplankton. The upper surface of the polyp columns is often bumpy and iridescent green or blue. *Isaurus* spp. are cryptic, occurring among algae on hardbottoms and on reef flats. They need bright light and regular night-time feeding to thrive.

Similar: *Protopalythoa*

Desireable/undesireable features: Ornamental. Reef safe.

Food: Carnivorous, filter feeder, photosynthetic.

Special considerations: Light. Weekly night-time feeding of zooplankton or substitute.

Hardiness in captivity: Growth and reproduction. Life span - years.

Typical appearance of *Isaurus* on a reef flat.

Isaurus tuberculatus at night, polyps feeding.

Isaurus tuberculatus typical daytime appearance, David Saxby's aquarium, London.

47

Parazoanthus and *Epizoanthus*

Common Name: Sponge zoanthid

Region: Circumtropical and temperate seas

Description: *Parazoanthus* and *Epizoanthus* live in association with sponges, hydroids, antipatharians or gorgonians, imbedded in or covering the tissue of their host. Their sting discourages fishes from eating sponges. *Epizoanthus* also grows on bare rock or in association with hermit crabs. Most are brown, yellow, orange, or red, and are not photosynthetic. Some may contain zooxanthellae.

Similar: *Acrozoanthus* and Yellow Polyps.

Desireable/undesireable features: Ornamental. Reef safe.

Food: Carnivorous, filter feeder, some are photosynthetic.

Special considerations: Water flow, daily supplemental feeding required. Sponge host may or may not be hardy.

Hardiness in captivity: Growth and reproduction. Life span - years (with care).

Red *Epizoanthus* sp. from the Eastern Pacific (Mexico). Living Seas Aquarium, Chicago.

Parazoanthus sp. from Japan, with polyps open.

Parazoanthus sp. on a sponge in the Solomon Islands.

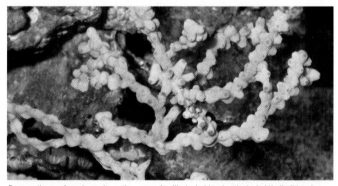

Parazoanthus sp. from Japan. It smothers a sea-fan-like hydroid, using the hydroid's *flexible axis.*

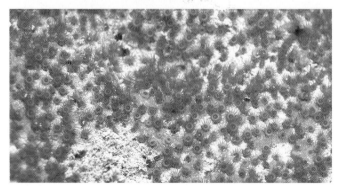

Parazoanthus or *Epizoanthus* on a sponge, Florida. It may have zooxanthellae, or brown pigment only.

Parazoanthus axinellae from the Mediterranean, Museo Oceanographique de Monaco.

Acrozoanthus

Common Name: Stick Polyps

Region: Indo-Pacific

Description: Soft columns and elongate brown tentacles with zooxanthellae. Commensal on the tubes of the annelid worm *Eunice*, which lives in shallow sand and mudflat or seagrass areas with strong tidal flow. The tops of the worm tubes are harvested (leaving the worm intact in the lower part of its home in the sand). In aquaria the polyps spread onto other substrates. A bluish or greenish species apparently belonging to this genus occurs on reef slopes among algae and tunicates in Indonesia.

Similar: *Parazoanthus*, *Epizoanthus*, Yellow Polyps.

Desireable/undesireable features: Ornamental. Reef safe.

Food: Carnivorous, filter feeder, photosynthetic.

Special considerations: Light. Water motion. Weekly feeding of meaty foods (zooplankton, tubifex worms, chopped shrimp).

Hardiness in captivity: Growth and reproduction. Life span - years (with care).

Acrozoanthus grows on the upper portion of parchment-like tube of the polychaete worm *Eunice*.

Acrozoanthus multiplies and spreads rapidly in aquaria when given strong light, currents, and food.

Undescribed Zoanthid

Common Name: Yellow Polyps

Region: Western Pacific

Description: Bright yellow or brownish yellow polyps with zooxanthellae and elongate tentacles. Colonies of clones may span several square metres. Polyps connected to each other at the pedal disc in clumps of usually not more than four, with many separate individuals. Encrusts coral rubble and algae on shallow reef flats and seagrass beds.

Similar: *Acrozoanthus* and *Parazoanthus*.

Desireable/undesireable features: Ornamental, Harmful to corals. Reef safe.

Food: Carnivorous, filter feeder, photosynthetic.

Special considerations: Light. Weekly feeding of meaty foods such as zooplankton, tubifex worms, chopped shrimp.

Hardiness in captivity: Growth and reproduction. Life span - years.

The unidentified yellow zoanthid called "Yellow Polyps" from Singapore, Kenny Tan.

Zoanthus

Common Name: Button Polyps, Polyp Rock, Zoanthids, False Coral, Colonial Anemones.

Region: Circumtropical and in some temperate regions.

Description: Mat-like colonies of polyps with a fringe of blunt tentacles surrounding the oral disc, in contrasting shades of green, red, orange, pink, and blue. Obtain most of their nutrition from their zooxanthellae. Some do, but most do not eat meaty foods (All eat dissolved organic matter). Some eat sea urchin eggs, chopped worms, or finely chopped fish.

Similar: *Protopalythoa* polyps are usually larger, and have tentacles that alternate up-down-up-down with pointed tips.

Desireable/undesireable features: Ornamental. Harmful to corals. Reef safe.

Food: Carnivorous, filter feeder, photosynthetic.

Special considerations: Light.

Hardiness in captivity: Growth and reproduction. Life span - years.

Zoanthus spp. are damaged by *Discosoma* spp., and should be separated from them.

Zoanthus sp. Aquarium photo at Zoomark, Milan Italy in the display of Corallarium.

Zoanthus sp.

50

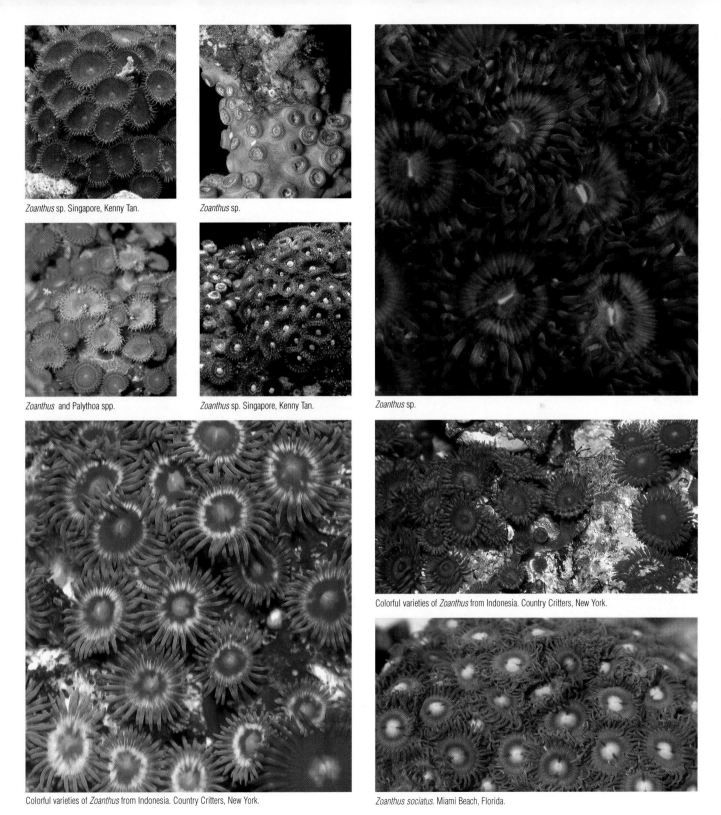

Zoanthus sp. Singapore, Kenny Tan.

Zoanthus sp.

Zoanthus and Palythoa spp.

Zoanthus sp. Singapore, Kenny Tan.

Zoanthus sp.

Colorful varieties of Zoanthus from Indonesia. Country Critters, New York.

Colorful varieties of Zoanthus from Indonesia. Country Critters, New York.

Zoanthus sociatus. Miami Beach, Florida.

51

Nemanthus

Common Name: Branch Anemone

Region: Indo-Pacific

Description: *Nemanthus annamensis* smothers gorgonians, taking over the branchy axis in much the same way as zoanthids of the genus *Parazoanthus.* Usually white but may also be orange or mottled.

Similar: *Parazoanthus* spp. The polyps of the stony coral *Tubastraea* are quite like the anemone *Nemanthus.*

Desireable/undesireable features: Ornamental, Harmful to corals. Reef safe.

Food: Carnivorous, filter feeder.

Special considerations: Water flow. Daily supplemental feeding of meaty foods such as zooplankton, tubifex worms, chopped shrimp.

Hardiness in captivity: Growth and reproduction. Life span - years (with care).

Nemanthus annamensis. Kushimoto, Japan.

Actinia

Common Name: Red Rock Anemone, Red Rose Anemone, Waratah Anemone, Tomato anemone

Region: Temperate and subtropical seas

Description: Small bright red or brownish-red anemone with a compact thick column that sometimes has blue spots. Intertidal. Common in tide pools. Frequently gives birth to small whole anemones. *Actinia equina* occurs in the Mediterranean, *A. tenebrosa* occurs in Australia, and other species occur in different temperate localities (such as south Africa) but in the same rocky habitat. Subtropical species are less colorful.

Similar: *Bunodosoma* spp. that live in tidepools in the tropics.

Desireable/undesireable features: Ornamental. Reef safe.

Food: Carnivorous, filter feeder.

Special considerations: Temperature between 65 degrees and 74 degrees Fahrenheit. Prefers strong water motion.

Hardiness in captivity: Growth and reproduction. Life span - years.

Actinia equina is a hardy intertidal anemone from the Mediterranean, but requires chilled water.

Bunodosoma from Florida is similar to *Actinia* and hardy. Caution: It eats small fishes!

Dofleinia

Common Name: None

Region: Western Pacific, including temperate regions in Japan

Description: Tentacles bright pink or brown with stripes. Prominent spots in a pattern on the tentacles are potent clusters of stinging cells. Lives on sandy bottoms with column buried. Sting is powerful, dangerous to fishes and painful or dangerous to humans.

Similar: none

Desireable/undesireable features: Ornamental. Reef safe. Harmful to fishes.

Food: Carnivorous, filter feeder. Feed large meaty foods.

Special considerations: Temperature. Some species require temperature between 65 degrees and 74 degrees Fahrenheit to thrive. Tropical species thrive at warmer temperatures. Requires sandy bottom.

Hardiness in captivity: Hardy.
Life span - years.

Dofleinia sp. Japan.

Condylactis

Common Name: Condy, Haitian Anemone

Region: Caribbean. Indo-Pacific accounts are likely other genera

Description: Elongate tentacles that may become swollen at tips, like *Entacmaea*. Commonly have purple pigment at the tips, and reddish pigment in the column.

Similar: *Entacmaea* and *Macrodactyla*.

Desireable/undesireable features: Ornamental. Reef safe. Harmful to fishes.

Food: Carnivorous, filter feeder. Feed large meaty foods. Photosynthetic.

Special considerations: Provide strong light. Strong water motion. Feed meaty foods a few times per month.

Hardiness in captivity: Hardy. Life span - years.

Condylactis gigantea often has a red column.

Condylactis gigantea on a shallow reef in the Bahamas.

Stichodactyla

Common Name: Carpet anemone

Region: Indo-Pacific, Caribbean

Description: *Stichodactyla* spp. are characterized by having numerous bead-like or fine finger like tentacles that give the appearance of a carpet. Stichodactyla *mertensii* is among the largest anemones, attaining disc diameters in excess of one metre. It has mostly short tentacles on the disc, with some more elongate tentacles near the mouth, and occurs on outer reefs in the Pacific to Indian Ocean in bright light and strong water flow. *Stichodactyla haddoni* sometimes occurs on reefs in deep water, but is more abundant on shallow reef flats or in lagoons and among seagrass, with its column buried in fine sand or coral rubble. *Stichodactyla giganteum* occurs in turbid lagoons with occasional strong tidal flow. *Stichodactyla helianthus* is the only Caribbean member of this genus, and it occurs on reefs and in seagrass beds.

Similar: *Cryptodendrum adhaesivum* from the Indo-Pacific region, *Actinoporus elegans* from the Caribbean.

Desireable/undesireable features: Ornamental. Reef safe. Harmful to fishes. Harmful to corals. Toxic to people.

Food: Carnivorous, filter feeder. Feed large meaty foods. Photosynthetic.

Special considerations: Light. Strong water motion. Harmed by pump intakes or overflow drains. See above description for substrate requirements.

Hardiness in captivity: Poor, generally. Growth and reproduction reported in aquaria (by budding, fission, and sexual reproduction). Life span- months - years (with care).

Green *Stichodactyla haddoni*. Aquarium photo, paris France.

Orange *Stichodactyla haddoni*. Oceanopolis. Brest, France.

Large *Stichodactyla haddoni* on a deep reef slope, Solomon Islands.

Stichodactyla sp. that mimics *Ricordea*. It may be *S. tapetum*. Paris, France.

Stichodactyla cf. *tapetum* with the shrimp *Thor amboinensis*. Kushimoto, Japan.

55

Stichodactyla mertensii with a pair of the hybrid cross of *Amphiprion sandaracinos* x *A. chrysopterus*.

Stichodactyla mertensii, here with a pair of *A. chrysopterus*, grows to more than 1 meter in diameter.

Stichodactyla helianthus reproduces prolifically by dividing in half. Ft. Lauderdale, Florida.

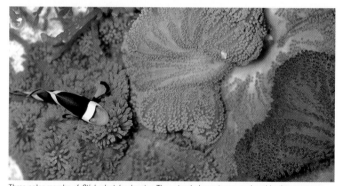

Three color morphs of *Stichodactyla gigantea*. The natural pigments are produced by the anemone.

Stichodactyla mertensii with a trio of anemonefish, *Amphiprion sandaracinos*. Solomon Islands.

Stichodactyla gigantea at the Löbbecke Museum and Aquazoo, Dusseldorf, Germany.

Heteractis

Common Name: Ritteri Anemone, Bulb-tip Anemone, Magnificent Anemone, Beaded Anemone, Malu Anemone, Sand Anemone, Long Tentacle Anemone

Region: Indo-Pacific, Red Sea

Description: *Heteractis magnifica* grows to enormous size, about 1 meter in diameter when solitary. In some regions they are smaller and form stands of clones produced vegetatively by fission. They require bright light and strong water flow, as they occur on reef pinnacles or exposed reef slopes, with the column exposed and attached to smooth coral rock. *Heteractis aurora*, the beaded anemone, has characteristic knobs on the tentacles and a striped oral region. It lives with its column buried in sand or coral rubble. *Heteractis malu* also has its column in sand, gravel or rubble, and has short tentacles. Young specimens may have beaded tentacles, like *H. aurora*. *Heteractis crispa* has numerous long pointed tentacles and is common on reefs, with its column attached in crevices in coral heads, but sometimes buried in coral rubble.

Similar: *Entacmaea* quadricolor has forms with a colorful base that resemble *H. magnifica*. *Macrodactyla* can be confused with *H. malu* and *H. crispa*. Young *Macrodactyla doreensis* may have beaded tentacles and are easily confused with *H. aurora*.

Desireable/undesireable features: Ornamental. Reef safe. Harmful to fishes. Harmful to corals.

Food: Carnivorous, filter feeder. Feed large meaty foods. Photosynthetic.

Special considerations: Light. Strong water motion. Harmed by pump intakes or overflow drains. See above description for substrate requirements.

Hardiness in captivity: Poor generally, but growth and reproduction (by fission) reported in aquariums. Life span - months - decades (with care).

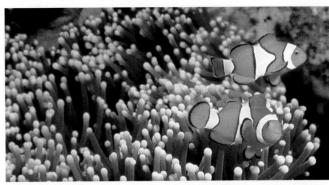
Amphiprion percula in *Heteractis magnifica* with coloring like *Euphyllia glabrescens*. Solomon Islands.

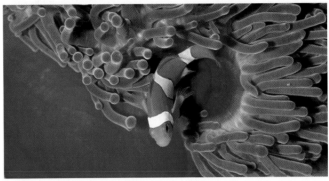
Heteractis magnifica with a bright red column. Solomon Islands.

Heteractis magnifica prefers strong currents and strong illumination. Solomon Islands.

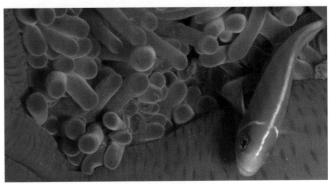
Heteractis magnifica with *Amphiprion perideraion*. Solomon Islands.

Heteractis crispa with *Amphiprion chrysopterus*. Solomon Islands.

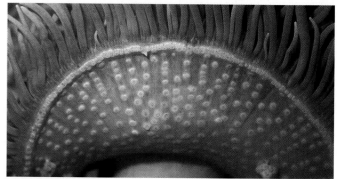

Heteractis crispa with a pair of *Amphiprion chrysopterus*. The female is a hybrid. Solomon Islands.

Heteractis crispa. Aquarium Photo.

The "beaded" tentacles of *Heteractis aurora*. Solomon Islands.

Heteractis aurora. Solomon Islands.

Heteractis malu. Solomon Islands.

Heteractis malu. Solomon Islands.

Macrodactyla

Common Name: Long Tentacle Anemone, Corkscrew Anemone

Region: Indo-Pacific

Description: Elongate tentacles that may curl at tips. Color variable. Oral disc often but not always striped. Column often but not always orange. Prominent verrucae on column. Occurs on sandy or muddy bottoms with column buried.

Similar: Large specimens may easily be confused with *Heteractis crispa.* The latter has more numerous tentacles. Small specimens of *M. doreensis* may have beaded tentacles like *Heteractis aurora, Phymanthus,* or small *H. malu. Entacmaea* may develop long tentacles like *Macrodactyla.*

Desireable/undesireable features: Ornamental. Reef safe. Harmful to fishes. Harmful to corals, but easily separated because of habit of living in sand.

Food: Carnivorous, filter feeder. Feed large meaty foods. Photosynthetic.

Special considerations: Light. Harmed by pump intakes or overflow drains. See above description for substrate requirements.

Hardiness in captivity: Growth and reproduction (by fission). Life span - years.

Macrodactyla doreensis in the natural habitat with *Amphiprion polymnus.* Solomon Islands.

Macrodactyla doreensis has prominent verrucae on the column. Such magenta specimens are prized.

Young *Macrodactyla doreensis* can have beaded tentacles like *Heteractis aurora* or *Phymanthus* spp.

An aquarium full of newly imported *Macrodactyla doreensis.* Note the red columns.

Macrodactyla doreensis is commonly called "Corkscrew Anemone" because of the curled tentacles.

Phymanthus

Common Name: Sand Anemone, Rock Anemone

Region: Circumtropical.

Description: Tentacles with beads or elaborate branches. Color variable, often cryptic. Oral disc often striped. Column often orange. Prominent verrucae on column. Occurs on sandy or muddy bottoms, seagrass beds, or attached to rock covered by a layer of sand or in rubble, with column buried.

Similar: Small specimens of *Heteractis aurora* and *M. doreensis* have beaded tentacles and red column. *Epicystis* of the Caribbean probably belongs to the same genus.

Desireable/undesireable features: Ornamental. Reef safe. Harmful to small fishes. Harmful to corals, but easily separated because of habit of living in sand.

Food: Carnivorous. Feed large meaty foods. Photosynthetic.

Special considerations: Light. Harmed by pump intakes or drains. See above description for substrate requirements.

Hardiness in captivity: Very Hardy. Life span - years.

Clownfish may adopt *Phymanthus* spp. as a host.

Colorful *Phymanthus* sp. is cryptic among seaweed coated reef rock. Solomon Islands.

Epicystis crucifer from the Caribbean is variable in appearance, but very much like *Phymanthus*.

Phymanthus muscosus. Solomon Islands.

Phymanthus muscosus. Solomon Islands.

Beautiful secondary branches on the tentacles of a *Phymanthus* sp. in Alf Nilsen's aquarium, Norway.

Phymanthus sp. A-Pet, Chicago, IL.

Entacmaea

Common Name: bubble Tip Anemone.

Region: Indo-Pacific, Red Sea.

Description: *Entacmaea quadricolor* is a variable species, forming "colonies" of small to medium sized clones in shallow water and large individuals in deeper water. Column with a distinctive collar just below the tentacles, and usually attached deeply within branchy corals. The tentacles often become swollen at the tips, hence the common name, and may be brown and green to bright red or pink. The column is usually just brownish, but some specimens from Fiji and Tonga have brightly colored columns.

Similar: Specimens with red or pink columns are strikingly similar to *Heteractis magnifica.* On coral near sandy bottoms *Entacmaea* is easily mistaken for *Macrodactyla doreensis.* "*Anemonia*" cf. *majano* seems very close to *Entacmaea.* In well-illuminated aquaria where both proliferate side by side, they seem to merge as one species (Rolf Hebbinghaus, pers com.), and it may be that one influences the other.

Desireable/undesireable features: Ornamental. Reef safe. Harmful to fishes. Harmful to some but not all corals.

Food: Carnivorous, filter feeder. Does not require supplemental feeding. Photosynthetic.

Special considerations: Light. Strong water motion. Harmed by pump intakes or overflow drains. See above description for substrate requirements.

Hardiness in captivity: Growth and reproduction (by fission and pedal laceration). Life span - years.

A "rose anemone," the red morph of *Entacmaea quadricolor.* Vivarium Karlsruh, Germany.

Small *Entacmaea quadricolor* may divide prolifically in aquariums, like *Anemonia* cf. *majano.*

E. quadricolor can resemble *M. doreensis.*

E. quadricolor has a "girdle" on the column.

The presence of bubble tips in *E. quadricolor* is variable. Musee Oceanographique de Monaco.

Anemonia

Common Name: Snake-locks anemone (For *Anemonia viridis* (=*sulcata*)

Region: Indo-Pacific, Mediterranean

Description: Three anemones appear to share this generic name, though they may not in fact belong to the same genus. *Anemonia viridis* (=*sulcata*) is a large bluish gray or green anemone with pink-tipped tentacles that occurs in the Mediterranean. "*Anemonia*" cf. *manjano* has bulb-tipped tentacles and is usually less than one inch in diameter, though it may reach a diameter of up to six inches. It may be green, brown, or gray, sometimes with white tentacle tips, and it proliferates rapidly, damaging adjacent corals. A related anemone looks like this one when small, but grows larger and develops a carpet of tentacles somewhat like *Heteractis* spp. It sometimes has purple pigment.

Similar: *Anemonia viridis* (=*sulcata*) is superficially similar to *Condylactis* spp. "*Anemonia*" cf. *manjano* seems very close to *Entacmaea*. The third anemone seems like a *Heteractis* sp. in its adult form, but probably belongs to a distinct genus.

Desireable/undesireable features: Ornamental. Reef safe. Harmful to fishes. Harmful to corals.

Food: Carnivorous, filter feeder. Photosynthetic. Does not require supplemental feeding.

Special considerations: Light. Strong water motion. *Anemonia viridis* (=*sulcata*) requires cool water temperatures, not above 74 degrees Fahrenheit.

Hardiness in captivity: Growth and reproduction. Life span - years.

Anemonia cf. *manjano* with green pigment.

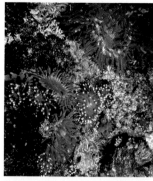

Two color forms of *Anemonia* cf. *manjano*.

This group of *Anemonia sp.* looks like a colony of zoanthids.

Unidentified *Anemonia?* sp.

Unidentified *Anemonia?* sp.

Anemonia viridis (=*sulcata*).

Anemonia cf. *manjano* multiply prolifically on live rock.

Cryptodendrum

Common Name: Pizza Anemone

Region: Indo-Pacific

Description: *Cryptodendrum adhaesivum* has finely branched short tentacles on the oral disc with a thin margin of differently branched tentacles that gives the impression of a pizza crust. In Japan the author observed a distinct anemone that appears to belong to this genus. Use caution when handling this anemone. It has a powerful sting.

Similar: *Stichodactyla, Heterodactyla*.

Desireable/undesireable features: Ornamental. Reef safe. Harmful to fishes. Harmful to corals. Toxic to people.

Food: Carnivorous, filter feeder. Feed chopped fish or shrimp. Photosynthetic.

Special considerations: Light. Strong water motion. Harmed by pump intakes or overflow drains.

Hardiness in captivity: Hardy. Life span - years.

Cryptodendrum adhaesivum, known as the "Pizza Anemone" with its *"pepperoni shrimp."*

Cryptodendrum adhaesivum with *Periclimenes brevicarpalis.* Note fluorescent mouth.

63

Heterodactyla

Common Name: None

Region: Indo-Pacific

Description: Flat oral disc with a dense carpet-like covering of finely branched tentacles. At the margin of the disc occur berry-like nematospheres that are usually very colorful.

Similar: *Cryptodendrum adhaesivum,* which has shorter tentacles and no nematospheres. *Thalassianthus aster* is similar but smaller, and its nematospheres are whitish.

Desireable/undesireable features: Ornamental. Reef safe. Harmful to fishes. Harmful to corals. Toxic to people.

Food: Carnivorous, filter feeder. Feed chopped fish or shrimp. Photosynthetic.

Special considerations: Light. Strong water motion. Harmed by pump intakes or overflow drains.

Hardiness in captivity: Very Hardy. Life span - years.

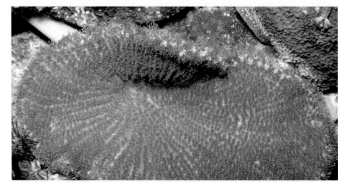

Heterodactyla hemprichii has its column attached under a ledge. Solomon Islands.

Heterodactyla hemprichii. Solomon Islands.

Thalassianthus aster, underside.

Thalassianthus aster has a potent sting!

Actineria sp? Solomon Islands.

Nematospheres of *Heterodactyla hemprichii.*

This anemone from the Solomon Islands is *Heterodactyla hemprichi.*

Actinodendron

Common Name: Hell's Fire Anemone, Tree Anemone

Region: Indo-Pacific

Description: Tentacles look like the branches of nephtheid soft corals. Potent sting. *Actinodendron glomeratum, A. plumosum*, and *A. arboreum* are common species.

Similar: *Megalactis hemprichii.*

Desireable/undesireable features: Ornamental. Reef safe. Harmful to fishes. Toxic to people.

Food: Carnivorous, filter feeder. Feed chopped fish or shrimp. Photosynthetic.

Special considerations: Light. Harmed by pump intakes or overflow drains. Provide sand substrate. Potent sting! The sting is reported to be excruciating, hence the common name.

Hardiness in captivity: Hardy. Life span - years.

A large *Actinodendron* sp. with its column buried in sand. Solomon Islands.

Megalactis hemprichii. Solomon Islands.

Closeup of the oral region of *Actinodendron* sp. An amazing thing to behold. But don't touch!

Bartholomea

Common Name: Curley-Cue Anemone

Region: Caribbean.

Description: Pale brown or blue with whitish knobby bands on elongate tentacles. In sandy areas. Associated with a pistol shrimp, and with the cleaner shrimp *Periclimenes pedersoni*.

Similar: *Aiptasia*, especially when small. Large *Bartholomea* may be mistaken for cerianthids. *Capnea lucida* from the Caribbean grows larger and has vesicles on the tentacles, quite like the coral *Euphyllia divisa*.

Desireable/undesireable features: Ornamental. Reef safe. Harmful to fishes.

Food: Carnivorous, filter feeder. Feed chopped fish or shrimp. Photosynthetic.

Special considerations: Light. Harmed by pump intakes or overflow drains.

Hardiness in captivity: Growth and reproduction (by pedal laceration). Life span - years.

The curleycue anemone, *Bartholomea annulata*.

Lebrunia

Common Name: Antler Anemone

Region: Caribbean

Description: *Lebrunia danae* has Zooxanthellae-filled, antler-like pseudotentacles with berry-like vesicles. At night these deflate and whitish tentacles extend to capture zooplankton. *Lebrunia coralligens*, with less-branched pseudotentacles and bright blue vessicles, occurs deeply imbedded in coral rock. Both have potent sting.

Similar: *Capnea lucida* from the Caribbean and *Triactis producta* from the Pacific.

Desireable/undesireable features: Ornamental. Reef safe. Harmful to fishes. Harmful to corals. Toxic to people.

Food: Carnivorous, filter feeder. Feed chopped fish or shrimp at night. Photosynthetic.

Special considerations: Light. Harmed by pump intakes or overflow drains. Harmful to small fishes. Toxic to humans.

Hardiness in captivity: Hardy. Life span- years.

Lebrunia danae, New Providence Island, Bahamas.

Lebrunia danae makes a spectacular exhibit in a small aquarium.

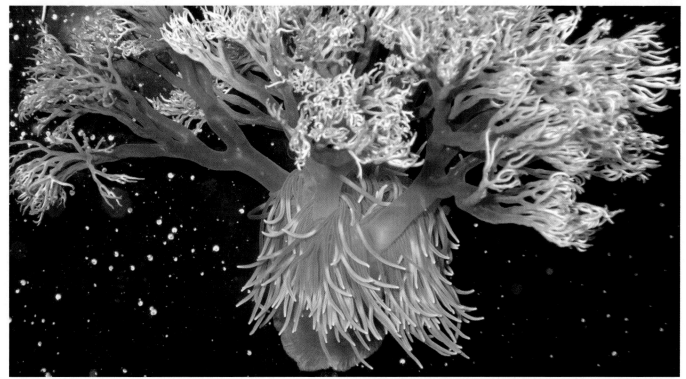

Lebrunia danae, aquarium photo in the early morning showing the pseudotentacles (upper, branched) and true tentacles (lower, stringy). World Class Aquarium, Brooklyn, New York.

Telmactis

Common Name: Club-Tipped Anemone

Region: Caribbean, Atlantic

Description: Tentacles have club shaped tips reminiscent of the ball tips on *Pseudocorynactis*. There may be more than one species or genus in the Caribbean. Sometimes very colorful. Though beautiful, *Telmactis* should not be harvested due to its very dangerous stinging ability.

Similar: *Pseudocorynactis*

Desireable/undesireable features: Ornamental. Reef safe. Harmful to fishes. Extremely toxic to people.

Food: Carnivorous, filter feeder. Feed chopped fish or shrimp.

Special considerations: Harmed by pump intakes or overflow drains. Potent sting! The nematocysts on the tentacle tips adhere so strongly that they can tear skin. The sting is reported to be excruciating and causes scars.

Hardiness in captivity: Very Hardy. Life span - years.

Telmactis cf. *americana*. Kathy Smith.

Discosoma and *Rhodactis*

Common Name: Mushroom anemone, Elephant Ear

Region: Red Sea, Indo-Pacific, Caribbean (absent Eastern Pacific???)

Description: Disc shaped corallimorphs with mainly smooth surface, but sometimes with bead-like vesicles or branched vesicles that look like tentacles

Similar: *Ricordea* and *Amplexidiscus*. The distinction between *Rhodactis* and *Discosoma* is so blurry that J. C. den Hartog, who worked on their taxonomy, preferred to group most into *Discosoma*.

Desireable/undesireable features: Ornamental. Reef safe. Harmful to corals upon contact.

Food: Photosynthetic. Carnivorous, filter feeder. Feed chopped fish or shrimp, chopped worms or tubifex.

Special considerations: Moderate, indirect light.

Hardiness in captivity: Growth and reproduction. Life span - years.

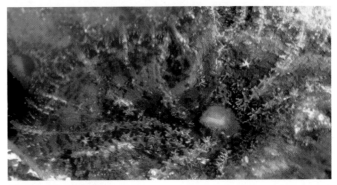

Discosoma carlgreni from Florida.

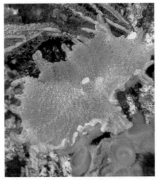

Discosoma neglecta. Riverbanks Zoo.

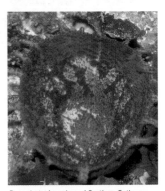

D. neglecta. Aquarium of Santiago Gutierrez.

Discosoma sp. 1. Indonesia

Discosoma sp. 1. Indonesia

A pectiniid stony coral that mimics *Discosoma*.

Rhodactis sp. with "pseudopolyp" tentacles.

Discosoma sp. 1. Singapore. Kenny Tan.

Discosoma sp. 1. Singapore. Kenny Tan.

Discosoma sp. 2. Singapore. Kenny Tan.

Discosoma sp. 2. Singapore. Kenny Tan.

Discosoma sp. 1. Indonesia. Fluorescent red form.

Discosoma sp. 1. Indonesia. Metallic blue form.

Discosoma sp. 1. Indonesia. Blue pinstripe form.

Rhodactis sp. Singapore, Kenny Tan.

Rhodactis sp. Singapore, Kenny Tan.

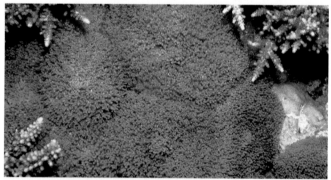

Rhodactis rhodostoma, Solomon Islands.

Rhodactis sp.

Rhodactis sp. Singapore, Kenny Tan.

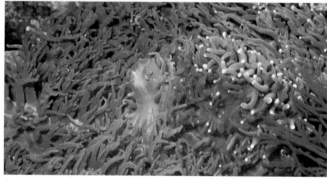

Rhodactis rhodostoma.

Rhodactis cf. *howesi*. Solomon Islands.

70

Rhodactis cf. *mussoides* has a thick tissue like mussid corals, and multiple mouths.

Rhodactis inchoata from the Solomon Islands.

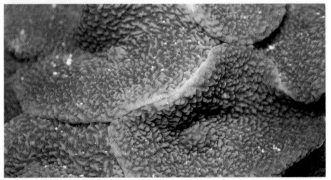

Rhodactis cf. *mussoides*, Fiji.

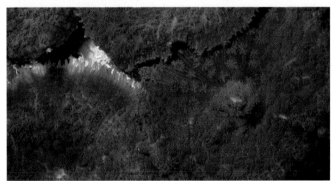

Rhodactis inchoata from Tonga.

"Giant Green Metallic Mushroom," and unidentified *Rhodactis* sp. from Indonesia.

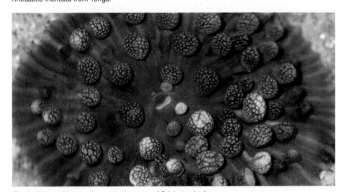

Rhodactis sanctithomae, form once known as "*Orinia torpida*.".

"Giant Green Metallic Mushroom," and unidentified *Rhodactis* sp. from Indonesia.

Rhodactis sanctithomae from the Caribbean.

71

Ricordea

Common Name: Ricordea. Florida False Coral

Region: Indo-Pacific, Caribbean

Description: Oral disc and margin with numerous bead-like vesicles that may at times become elongate like tentacles.

Similar: Some *Discosoma* spp. have bead-like vesicles on the oral disc. In fact there is a spectrum of appearance in *Discosoma*, from no beads to many beads to *Ricordea*-like! *Ricordea* is separate from *Discosoma* on the basis of having spirocysts. Small carpet anemones, *Stichodactyla* spp. and *Actinoporus elegans* are easily confused with *Ricordea*.

Desireable/undesireable features: Ornamental. Reef safe. Harmful to corals upon contact.

Food: Photosynthetic. Carnivorous, filter feeder. Feed chopped fish or shrimp, chopped worms or tubifex.

Special considerations: Light.

Hardiness in captivity: Growth and reproduction. Life span - years.

Fluorescent mouths on a *Ricordea florida*.

Rare color varieties of *Ricordea yuma* from Indonesia. Reef International, Milan, Italy.

Ricordea florida, aquarium photo, Toronto Canada.

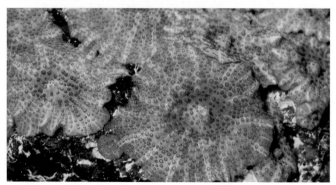
These *Discosoma* sp. have vessicles quite like the tentacles of *Ricordea*. Aquarium Karlsruh, Germany.

Ricordea yuma, from Singapore, Kenny Tan.

72

Ricordea yuma, typical form.

A spectacular *Ricordea yuma* from Indonesia. Reef International, Milan, Italy.

Ricordea florida can have brilliant colors.

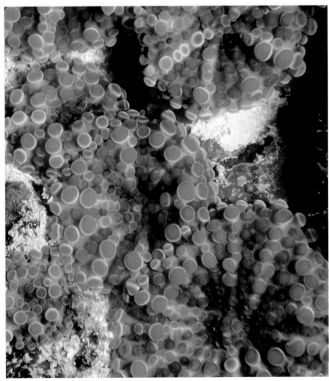

Ricordea cf. *yuma*, Solomon Islands.

Amplexidiscus

Common Name: Giant Elephant Ear (mushroom) anemone

Region: Indo-Pacific

Description: Very large (oral disk to more than 14 inches) corallimorph with tentacles on the oral disc except for a naked region near the margin. Traps fishes slowly without stinging them, like a "venus flytrap." Potentially capable of eating fishes at any time, but normally fishes know to avoid it.

Similar: *Discosoma* spp.

Desireable/undesireable features: Ornamental. Reef safe. Harmful to corals upon contact. Harmful to fishes.

Food: Photosynthetic. Carnivorous. Feed chopped fish or shrimp, chopped worms or tubifex.

Special considerations: Light.

Hardiness in captivity: Growth and reproduction. Life span - years.

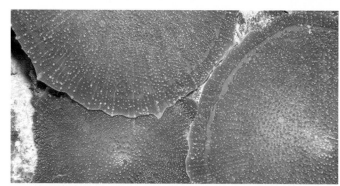
Amplexidiscus fenestrafer, among the largest Corallimorphs, traps and eats fish.

Amplexidiscus fenestrafer has a "naked" tentacle-free ring near the margin of the disc.

Corynactis

Common Name: Strawberry Anemone

Region: Circumtropical and in temperate seas.

Description: Very anemone-like, with elongate tentacles, each with a white ball-shaped tip. Often very colorful in shades of pink, red, orange or with iridescent hues. Column cryptically colored or very colorful. Occurs mainly in shady regions of the reef. Most abundant in cool temperate regions.

Similar: *Pseudocorynactis* spp., *Corallimorphus.*

Desireable/undesireable features: Ornamental. Reef safe. Harmful to corals, clams, snails, and crustaceans upon contact. Harmful to fishes. Powerful sting that may be toxic to people.

Food: Carnivorous. Feed (daily) chopped fish or shrimp, chopped worms or tubifex, or flake foods.

Special considerations: Temperate species require cool water below 72 degrees Fahrenheit.

Hardiness in captivity: Growth and reproduction. Life span - years.

Corynactis californica. Monterey Bay Aquarium.

A tropical *Corynactis* sp. Note the new buds at the base produced by pedal laceration.

Pseudocorynactis

Common Name: Orange Ball Anemone

Region: Indo-Pacific, Caribbean

Description: Very anemone-like, with elongate tentacles that each have a ball shaped tip that may be white or orange. Column is usually cryptically colored to blend with rocks, but sometimes is very colorful. *Pseudocorynactis caribbeorum* expands at night primarily, and quickly contracts in response to light. The Indo-Pacific *Pseudocorynactis* species remains expanded at all times and is not sensitive to light, though it occurs only in shady regions of the reef. Seldom harvested for the aquarium trade, but easy to propagate by fission. A worthwhile aquaculture subject.

Similar: *Corynactis* spp., the strawberry anemones common especially in temperate regions, but also occurring in the tropics. *Corallimorphus*, a deepwater genus.

Desireable/undesireable features: Ornamental. Reef safe. Harmful to corals, clams, snails, and crustaceans upon contact. Harmful to fishes. Powerful sting that may be toxic to people.

Food: Carnivorous. Feed chopped fish or shrimp, chopped worms or tubifex, or flake foods.

Special considerations: The Indo-Pacific species is not safe to house with fishes or mobile invertebrates because it will catch and eat them. Best kept in an aquarium by itself.

Hardiness in captivity: Growth and reproduction. Life span - years.

A spectacularly colored *Pseudocorynactis caribbaeorum* given to the author by Eric Reichardt.

This *Pseudocorynactis caribbaeorum* collected by Eric Reichardt has divided into four polyps.

Pseudocorynactis sp. collected by Tony Nahacky, Fiji.

Pseudocorynactis sp. from Fiji is a very active predator of fishes and invertebrates.

75

Cerianthus, Pachycerianthus, Arachnanthus

Common Name: Cerianthus Anemone, Tube Dwelling Anemone

Region: Circumtropical and in temperate seas

Description: Column in a parchment-like tube made by specialized nematocysts called ptychocysts, layered with mucus secretions. Normally buried, in soft sand, mud, or coral rubble. Slender elongate tentacles on the periphery of the oral disc and numerous finer tentacles surrounding mouth. Some species may have a powerful sting, but most Cerianthids are safe to house with fishes and invertebrates.

Similar: Some true sea anemones, such as *Bartholomea*.

Desireable/undesireable features: Ornamental. Reef safe. Harmful to some crustaceans. Some species harmful to fishes.

Food: Carnivorous. Feed *Artemia* nauplii, chopped fish or shrimp, chopped worms or tubifex, or flake foods.

Special considerations: Feed daily. Sand or gravel substrate.

Hardiness in captivity: Hardy. Life span - years.

Colorful cerianthid from Indonesia.

Colorful cerianthid from Indonesia.

Cerianthid exhibit at the Shedd Aquarium, Chicago.

Cerianthid "anemones" live in sand or mud bottoms and construct a tube dwelling.

Antipathes, Cirripathes, Stichopathes,

Common Name: Black Coral, Wire Coral, Whip Coral, Sea Whip

Region: Circumtropical

Description: Wire-like, whip, spring-shaped, bottle-brush or bush-like growths with a flexible horny axis. Polyps with usually six finger-like tentacles. Most abundant growing from current swept walls on reefs in deep water, but some species can be found in quiet recesses, caves, or inside shipwrecks, and others are common on reef slopes in shallow water in bright sunlight.

Similar: May be confused with gorgonians and certain hydroids, such as *Solanderia*.

Desireable/undesireable features: Ornamental. Reef safe.

Food: Carnivorous. Feed *Artemia* nauplii, chopped fish or shrimp, chopped worms or tubifex, or flake foods.

Special considerations: Requires daily feeding of large quantities of food to thrive. Thick-stemmed wire types are easy to maintain and grow in aquariums, while finer branched ones are more difficult (J. Charles Delbeek, pers. comm.).

Hardiness in captivity: Growth and reproduction in some but not all species. Life span - years.

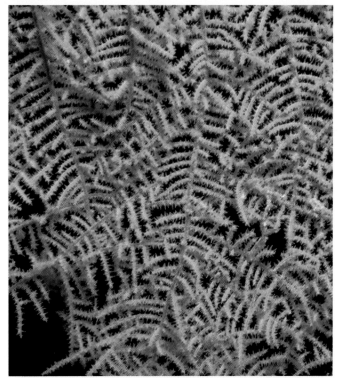

Antipathes sp. seafan composed of fine interconnected pinnate branches, Solomon Islands.

Antipathes sp. composed of fine dichotomous branches, Solomon Islands.

Stichopathes sp. with the crab *Xenocarcinus tuberculatus*. Japan.

Cirripathes sp. forming a corkscrew shape. Solomon Islands.

Chapter Three

Coeloplana

Common Name:

Region: Indo-Pacific, Caribbean

Description: transparent flat amorphous and highly mobile, these delicate creatures unfurl two extremely fine elongate tentacles into the water to trap planktonic food. The tentacles collapse in an instant into an apparent tangle and then just as quickly unfurl in neat perfection. Fascinating to watch. Able to swim with flapping motion. Harvested incidentally with soft corals (especially *Sarcophyton* spp.) and with algae, (especially *Caulerpa* spp.). *Coeloplana astericola* occurs with the sea *star Echinaster luzonicus.*

Similar: May be confused with flatworms.

Desireable/undesireable features: Ornamental. Reef safe.

Food: Carnivorous. Feed marine snow and tiny zooplankton.

Special considerations: None.

Hardiness in captivity: Growth and reproduction.
Life span - months - years.

Coeloplana astericola is a commensal on *Echinaster luzonicus.* Max Gibbs.

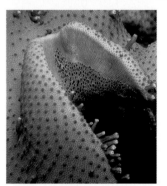

Coeloplana sp. on *Sarcophyton.*

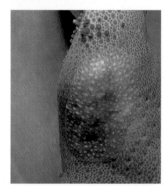

Coeloplana sp. on *Sarcophyton.*

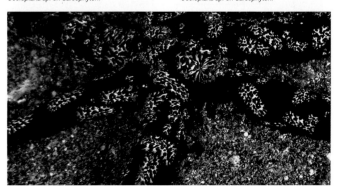

A large number of *Coeloplana astericola* on a dark specimen of *Echinaster luzonicus.* Max Gibbs.

Flatworms

latworms belong to the phylum Platyhelminthes, which includes the familiar freshwater planarian, *Dugesia*, famous for laboratory demonstrations of its regenerative capabilities. The name flatworm is misleading since these creatures are not related to annelid worms.

Flatworms are primarily marine organisms. Most are benthic, a few are able to swim by coordinated undulating movement, and there are also a few planktonic species that adhere to drifting seaweed. There are freshwater species and quite a few terrestrial species as well. Movement is accomplished mainly through the propulsive force of tiny cilia, but also through muscular undulations and contractions of the body. Flatworms also lay down mucus as they crawl on the substrate.

Flatworms feed on a variety of things, depending on the species. Many consume bacteria and organic matter. Some small species live interstitially, feeding on organic matter among sand grains. Some eat protozoans, tiny crustaceans such as copepods, specific invertebrates such as colonial tunicates, or the mucus and trapped organisms from the surface of specific invertebrates. Others consume microalgae. A few species that feed on hydroids are able to incorporate their prey's nematocysts in their own body wall for defense, in much the same manner as sea slugs that feed on cnidarians. Like some sea slugs, some flatworms are also photosynthetic, possessing symbiotic algae. These special forms are common on the sun-exposed surfaces of shallow reefs, adjacent sand or rubble zones, on corals and other cnidarians, and on the blades of seagrasses.

Flatworms include many commensal and parasitic species. The class Turbellaria includes some parasites, but flatworms in the class Trematoda and Cestoda are entirely parasitic, including the well known tapeworm among other parasites such as flukes and roundworms.

A few types of acoel flatworms, members of a special order that lacks a gut cavity, are common and hardy aquarium inhabitants. Introduced with live rock and sand, corals, corallimorpharians, and clams, they grow and reproduce in aquaria. Some common photosynthetic species are pests that bloom in plague proportions. It is known that sea slugs of the genus *Chelidonura* feed on these acoel flatworms. Certain polyclad flatworms, large and colorful species that often mimic sea slugs, may also feed on the pest acoel species, but this has not yet been observed.

Convolutriloba

Common Name: Red Flatworm, Red Planarian

Region: Western Pacific

Description: *Convolutriloba retrogemma* is red, brown, or orange, squarish and small, up to about 1/4 inch total length but usually smaller. Able to reproduce by fragmentation, it is a plague species that blooms in strongly illuminated zones with low water velocities.

Similar: *Amphiscolops*, *Waminoa*, and other small acoel flatworms.

Desireable/undesireable features: Toxic to fishes. Reef safe.

Food: Herbivorous, photosynthetic.

Special considerations: Population explosions controlled by seaslugs of the genus *Chelidonura* that eat flatworms. Strong water motion limits the areas where they can survive.

Hardiness in captivity: Growth and reproduction. Life span - weeks - months - years.

Waminoa

Common Name: Planarian

Region: Caribbean, Atlantic, Mediterranean, & Western Pacific

Description: Disk shaped pale brown green, or gray with a whitish median line or pale ring at the periphery. Commonly found crawling on the surface of cnidarians, especially *Discosoma* spp., large polyped stony corals, and soft corals. Photosynthetic. Able to reproduce by fragmentation. May develop prolifically and cover corals.

Similar: May be confused with platyctene ctenophores such as *Coeloplana* spp.

Desireable/undesireable features: Mildly harmful to corals and corallimorpharia. Reef safe.

Food: Herbivorous, photosynthetic.

Special considerations: Population explosions controlled by seaslugs of the genus *Chelidonura* that eat flatworms.

Hardiness in captivity: Growth and reproduction. Life span - weeks - months - years.

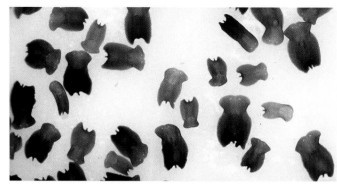
Convolutriloba retrogemma. The Red planarian that proliferates in plague proportions.

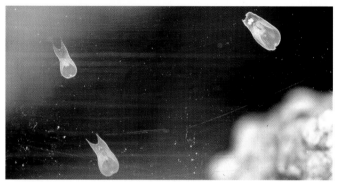
Amphiscolops sp. is a harmless planarian that feeds on copepods. It is common in reef aquariums.

Waminoa sp. on the stony coral *Goniopora* sp. Solomon Islands.

Waminoa sp. on a *Discosoma* sp. corallimorph. Aquarium photo.

Pseudobiceros and *Pseudoceros*

Common Name: None

Region: Circumtropical

Description: Large, often brightly colored flatworms. Mimic sea slugs. May have folds in the margin that form "pseudotentacles" that look like the antennae of sea slugs. Swift crawlers and able to swim by undulating margin.

Similar: Other genera of similar flatworms include *Phrikoceros, Paraplanaria, Thysanozoon, Maiazoon, Acanthozoon, Eurylepta, Callioplana,* and *Bulaceros*

Desireable/undesireable features: Ornamental. Some may be toxic to fishes. Reef safe.

Food: Carnivorous and/or detritivore. Colonial tunicates, mucus and detritus.

Special considerations: Harmed by pump intakes or overflow drains. Special Diet.

Hardiness in captivity: Poor for most species, with a few exceptions for the detritivores. Life span- weeks - months.

Pseudoceros sapphirinus. Solomon Islands.

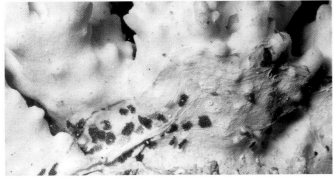

This unidentified flatworm eats acroporid corals.

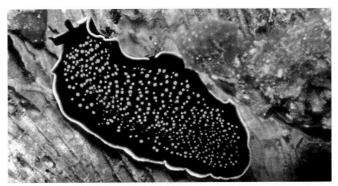

Thysanozoon nigropapillosum. Solomon Islands.

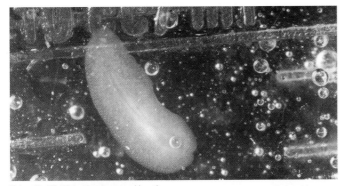

The egg masses of the *Acropora*-eating flatworm.

Pseudoceros pardalis from Puerto Rico. Photographed in the author's aquarium by Alf J. Nilsen.

Mollusks

Mollusks are a very diverse group that includes the snails, slugs, clams, mussels, oysters, limpets, chitons, and the highly advanced cephalopods such as octopus, squid, cuttlefish, and chambered nautilus. There are also less commonly observed mollusks, such as pelagic heteropods, thecostomes, pteropods, and gymnosomes that live in the open sea, worm like solenogasters that live on reefs, and scaphopods that build tusk-like shells and live in sandbeds.

In aquariums mollusks are both functional and ornamental. Various herbivorous snails are used for the control of algae, for instance. The several species of giant clams from tropical reefs in the Red Sea and Indo-Pacific regions have ornamental shells well known in the curio trade, but the mantles of the living clams are even more ornamental. This fact is appreciated by reef aquarium hobbyists who keep and grow giant clams in their home aquariums. Giant clams, which are now supplied farm-raised to the aquarium industry, also filter nitrogenous waste from the water, so their presence in the aquarium is functional as well. Limpets, with their Chinese-hat-like shells and Chitons, distinguished by their 8 articulating plates are mostly herbivores, and they are commonly introduced into aquariums with live rock substrates. Many species reproduce and proliferate in aquariums.

The fantastic flame scallops, *Lima* spp. are filter feeding clams that subsist, as most clams do, by feeding on bacteria, phytoplankton, dissolved organic material, and detritus in the water.

Although public aquariums successfully feature them, the Cephalopods are not recommended to the casual aquarium hobbyist since they require special care and do not belong in the typical "community" aquarium. Chambered nautilus, occasionally offered for sale in the aquarium market, require chilled water (below 68 °F) to thrive in captivity.

The amazingly colored sea slugs and their relatives are for the most part not suitable for aquariums, since they have special diets consisting of a particular species of sponge, hydroid, tunicate, or bryozoan. A few of them, however, are useful additions to aquariums because they eat nuisance algae or "plague" creatures such as flatworms, bristle worms, or *Aiptasia* spp. anemones.

Elysia

Common Name: Green Sea Slug, Lettuce Slug.

Region: Circumtropical and temperate seas.

Description: Green, yellow or brown with two flap like appendages (parapodia). Photosynthetic, incorporating in their tissues chloroplasts from the algae they eat. *Elysia* (=*Tridachia*) *crispata* from the Caribbean has frilly highly folded parapodia. It is ornately colored, with white, red, pink, and blue markings. *Elysia* (=*Tridachiella*) *diomedea* from the Eastern Pacific is similar.

Similar: *Aplysia, Cyerce, Plakobranchus,* and *Oxynoe* spp.

Desirable/undesirable features: Ornamental. Useful in reef aquariums. Reef safe.

Food: Herbivorous. Green Algae. Photosynthetic.

Special considerations: Harmed by pump intakes or drains. Must have light and sufficient green algae to thrive.

Hardiness in captivity: Growth and reproduction. Life span - months - years.

Elysia sp. Solomon Islands.

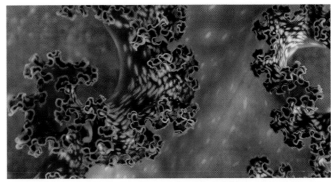

Closeup of the highly folded parapodia of *Elysia diomedea* from Costa Rica.

Plakobranchus spp., like *Elysia* spp., eat green algae and may be useful herbivores in aquariums.

Elysia diomedea from Costa Rica feeds on green filamentous algae.

Bright blue color morph of *Elysia crispata* from Florida.

Cyerce

Common Name: Glass Slug

Region: Red Sea, Indian, and Pacific Oceans

Description: *Cyerce nigricans*, the most colorful species in this genus, feeds on the green filamentous alga *Chlorodesmis*. It is not known whether it would feed on other green filamentous algae (for example *Derbesia* and *Bryopsis*), but it might. A captive breeding program to supply this beautiful creature might be a worthwhile venture. Other *Cyerce* spp. are less colorful but also feed on filamentous green algae.

Similar: *Elysia* spp.

Desirable/undesirable features: Ornamental. Useful in reef aquariums. Reef safe.

Food: Herbivorous. Photosynthetic.

Special considerations: Harmed by pump intakes or drains. Must have light and sufficient green algae to thrive.

Hardiness in captivity: Growth and reproduction. Life span - months - years.

Cyerce nigricans. Bruce Carlson.

Cyerce sp. Marj Awai.

Aplysia

Common Name: Sea Hare

Region: Tropical and temperate seas

Description: Rabbit-ear-like sensory folds on the head. Mantle with wing-like flaps used for swimming. Large species release purple dye when alarmed. Though only mildly toxic, this can pollute an aquarium.

Similar: *Bursatella, Dolabella, Dolabrifera, Stylocheilus.*

Desirable/undesirable features: Ornamental. Useful in reef aquariums. Small species are Reef safe. Large species not safe for aquariums. Toxic to fishes.

Food: Herbivorous. Red and green seaweeds. *Bursatella, Dolabrifera,* and *Stylocheilus* feed on cyanobacteria, and may be used to control nuisance algae common in aquariums. Small *Aplysia* spp. eat filamentous green algae.

Special considerations: Harmed by pump intakes or drains. Must have sufficient Red and green algae to thrive.

Hardiness in captivity: Hardy. Life span - months - years.

The charming rabbit-like face of *Aplysia californica*, photographed at the Monterey Bay Aquarium.

Elysia subornata from Florida could be confused with a small *Aplysia* sp.

Dolabella auricularia. aquarium photo, Paris, France.

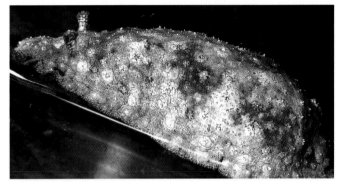

Dolabrifera dolabrifera looks a bit like a flattened Hippopotamus.

Aplysia sp. "taking flight" on a seagrass bed. They can swim quite rapidly this way.

91

Bulla

Common Name: Bubble Snail

Region: Circumtropical

Description: Small seaslugs with a thin bubble-shaped shell, common on intertidal mudflats and sand around seagrasses on in tidepools among algae. May burrow in sand and emerge at night to feed. Can reproduce prolifically in aquaria.

Similar: Several similar related genera, including *Haminoea*, and *Micromelo*.

Desirable/undesirable features: Ornamental. Useful in reef aquariums. Reef safe.

Food: Herbivorous. Feeds on filamentous algae and diatoms. May also feed on dead animals or polychaete worms.

Special considerations: Harmed by pump intakes or overflow drains. Must have sufficient algae to thrive.

Hardiness in captivity: Growth and reproduction. Life span - months - years.

Bulla striata, Virginia Key, Florida.

Bulla striata burrows quickly.

The shell of a large *Bulla striata*.

Melanochlamys

Common Name: Sea Slug

Region: Western Pacific

Description: Members of this genus live on sand, gravel or coral rubble areas and feed on polychaete worms, sucking them in like noodles. Their outline is similar to *Chelidonura* spp. Coloration is usually cryptic. These may be useful for the control of bristle worms in reef aquariums.

Similar: *Chelidonura*, *Navanax*, and *Philinopsis* spp. are similarly shaped and colored

Desirable/undesirable features: Ornamental. Useful in reef aquariums. Reef safe.

Food: Carnivorous.

Special considerations: Harmed by pump intakes or overflow drains. Must have sufficient polychaete worms to eat in order to thrive.

Hardiness in captivity: Unknown. Life span - months.

Melanochlamys sp. from Indonesia. Max Gibbs.

Chelidonura

Common Name: Head Shield Nudibranch

Region: Circumtropical

Description: Members of this genus feed on flatworms, and have essentially the same outline as their prey, with a hammerhead and two appendages at the rear. Many are brightly colored

Similar: *Melanochlamys, Navanax,* and *Philinopsis* spp. are similarly shaped and colored

Desirable/undesirable features: Ornamental. Useful in reef aquariums. Reef safe.

Food: Carnivorous. Feed on flatworms only.

Special considerations: Harmed by pump intakes or overflow drains. Must have flatworms to eat in order to thrive.

Hardiness in captivity: Growth. Spawning reported but successful reproduction in captivity not reported.
Life span - months.

Chelidonura varians has the same outline as the flatworms it eats.

Chelidonura varians. Solomon Islands.

Chelidonura electra. Solomon Islands.

Phyllodesmium

Common Name: None.

Region: Red Sea, Indian and Pacific Oceans.

Description: This genus includes several species that feed exclusively on soft corals. They incorporate zooxanthellae from their prey in their own tissues. Most do not cause much damage to their host, but large numbers of them could potentially do harm.

Similar: Melibe.

Desirable/undesirable features: Ornamental. Destructive or harmful to corals. Reef safe.

Food: Herbivorous. Photosynthetic.

Special considerations: Harmed by pump intakes or overflow drains. Must have sufficient light and soft coral hosts to thrive.

Hardiness in captivity: Growth and reproduction.
Life span - months - years.

P. briareum eats *Pachyclavularia* and *Briareum.*

Phyllodesmium magnum. Atlantis, L. I., NY.

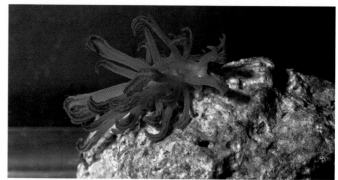

Phyllodesmium sp. that feeds on *Xenia* spp. Its cirri perfectly match *Xenia* polyps. J. C. Delbeek.

Phyllodesmium longicirra feeding on a *Sarcophyton* sp. leather coral. Papua New Guinea. Alan Storace. Note the golden brown zooxanthellae in its cirri.

Hexabranchus

Common Name: Spanish Dancer

Region: Circumtropical.

Description: *Hexabranchus sanguineus* is the largest of all nudibranchs, attaining a size of up to 60 cm (that's two feet!). Color is bright red, orange, pink, white and violet. Has six separate gills that may be withdrawn into "pockets," and wing-like parapodia with intense color. Swims by undulating these red and white parapodia, which explains its common name. This nudibranch starves in aquariums and thus should not be harvested.

Similar: None

Desirable/undesirable features: Ornamental. Reef safe.

Food: Carnivorous. Feeds on sponges.

Special considerations: Harmed by pump intakes or overflow drains. Must have sufficient food to thrive. Feeds on several types of (but not all) sponges.

Hardiness in captivity: Poor. Life span - weeks - months.

Hexabranchus spp. have colorful egg masses.

Hexabranchus sanguineus open their brightly colored mantles when disturbed.

Chromodoris and *Hypselodoris*

Common Name: Sea Slug, Sea Goddess

Region: Circumtropical

Description: Very colorful sea slugs with an oval shape, a flat rim of mantle around the periphery, prominent rhinophores on the head and a flower-like tuft of gills to the rear. They feed on sponges. Despite the lack of food, some specimens survive for several months in an aquarium, a significant amount of the natural life span. Nevertheless these creatures should not be harvested for aquaria as most specimens starve and/or die within a few weeks.

Similar: *Gymnodoris, Nembrotha, Risbecia.*

Desirable/undesirable features: Ornamental. Reef safe.

Food: Carnivorous. Feeds on sponges.

Special considerations: Harmed by pump intakes or overflow drains. Must have sufficient food to thrive. Feed on several types of (but not all) sponges.

Hardiness in captivity: Poor. Life span - weeks - months.

Chromodoris kuniei. Solomon Islands.

Hypselodoris cf. *bullocki* crawls on a sponge. Reef International, Milan, Italy.

Chromodoris willani. Solomon Islands.

Hypselodoris edenticulata from Florida is beautiful but not suitable for aquariums.

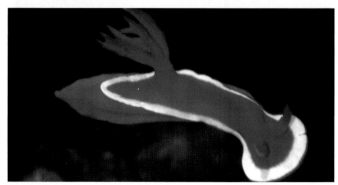

Hypselodoris cf. *bullocki.* Several color morphs belong to a complex of closely related species.

96

Nembrotha

Common Name: Nudibranch

Region: Red Sea, Indian and Pacific Oceans

Description: Very colorful nudibranchs found on coral reefs where they feed mainly on bryozoans of the genus *Bugula*, but also on colonial tunicates. Despite the lack of food, some specimens survive for several months in an aquarium, a significant amount of the natural life span. Nevertheless these creatures should not be harvested for aquaria as most specimens starve and/or die within a few weeks.

Similar: *Gymnodoris*

Desirable/undesirable features: Ornamental. Reef safe.

Food: Carnivorous. Feeds on bryozoans and colonial tunicates.

Special considerations: Harmed by pump intakes or overflow drains. Must have sufficient food to thrive.

Hardiness in captivity: Poor. Life span - weeks - months.

Nembrotha cristata feeds on colonial tunicates. Solomon Islands.

Closeup photo of the gills of a *Gymnodoris* sp. They resemble *Nembrotha* spp., but eat other seaslugs!

Nembrotha kubaryana has a variable color pattern. It feeds on branchy bryozoans. Solomon Islands.

Berghia

Common Name: Berghia

Region: Circumtropical and in temperate regions

Description: *Berghia verrucicornis* is a brown, white and blue nudibranch that looks like the small anemones upon which it feeds. It is occasionally available tank raised for aquariums to control the problematic plague anemones of the genus *Aiptasia*. Several species exist around the world.

Similar: Many Aeolid nudibranchs have similar appearance.

Desirable/undesirable features: Useful in reef aquariums. Reef safe.

Food: Carnivorous. Photosynthetic. Feeds on *Aiptasia* spp. anemones.

Special considerations: Harmed by pump intakes or drains. Must have light and sufficient *Aiptasia* to thrive.

Hardiness in captivity: Growth and reproduction. Life span-months. Not very hardy and easily lost in a large reef aquarium before it can establish a breeding population.

Berghia cf. *verrucicornis* from Inland Aquatics, Terre Haute, Indiana.

Pteraeolidia

Common Name: Nudibranch

Region: Red Sea, Indian and Pacific Oceans

Description: *Pteraeolidia ianthina* is elongate with numerous brown cirri with bluish highlights. Has good potential for aquaculture as it is useful in the control of the photosynthetic hydroid *Myrionema*. It incorporates the hydroid's symbiotic zooxanthellae in its own tissues, where they multiply and produce food for the nudibranch.

Similar: Many Aeolid nudibranchs have similar appearance.

Desirable/undesirable features: Useful in reef aquariums. Reef safe.

Food: Carnivorous. Photosynthetic. Feeds on *Hydroids*.

Special considerations: Harmed by pump intakes or drains. Must have light and sufficient *Hydroids* to thrive.

Hardiness in captivity: Growth and reproduction. Life span-months. Delicate to transfer to new aquaria. Often disappears without establishing a breeding population.

Pteraeolidia ianthina. Solomon Islands.

Phyllidia

Common Name: Warty Sea Slug

Region: Red Sea, Indian and Pacific Oceans

Description: Oval shaped with a thick warty mantle and no dorsal gills. Often very colorful. Members of this and the related genera listed below primarily feed on sponges. While beautiful to look at, these creatures generally starve in aquariums. Worse than that, some are very toxic and may kill fishes or other creatures housed in the same aquarium.

Similar: Related to and similar in appearance to *Phyllidiella*, *Phyllidiopsis*, *Fryeria*, *Ceratophyllidia*, and *Reticulidia*.

Desirable/undesirable features: Ornamental. Reef safe. Toxic to fishes. Toxic to other invertebrates.

Food: Carnivorous. Feed on sponges.

Special considerations: Harmed by pump intakes or overflow drains. Must have specific types of sponges to thrive. Toxic to fishes and other invertebrates.

Hardiness in captivity: Poor. Life span - weeks - months.

Phyllidia elegans, Solomon Islands.

Phyllidia tula, Solomon Islands.

Phyllidia ocellata, Japan.

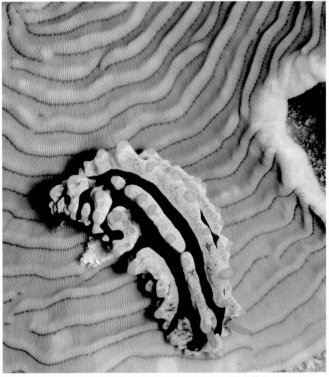

Phyllidia varicosa, Solomon Islands. This species is very toxic and may kill all life in an aquarium.

Turbo

Common Name: Turbo Snail, Turban Snail, Top-Shell

Region: Circumtropical and some temperate regions.

Description: Top-shaped snails with thick shells, an irridescent interior and usually a thick shelly operculum. Commonly used for control of algae in aquariums.

Similar: *Astraea* and *Trochus* spp.

Desirable/undesirable features: Useful in reef aquariums. Reef safe.

Food: Herbivorous. Filamentous and fleshy algae, cyanobacteria and diatoms.

Special considerations: Cool temperature for specimens collected from the Gulf of California. May starve in aquaria with inadequate supply of fleshy algae. Offer dried seaweed (Nori) as food if the rocks are bare.

Hardiness in captivity: Growth and reproduction. Life span - months - years.

Turbo spp. are popular algae grazing snails.

Turbo cf. *setosus* from the central to southwest Pacific.

Turbo castanea, the Chestnut Turban from Florida has variable shell color and ornamentation.

101

Astraea

Common Name: Star Snail

Region: Circumtropical and some temperate regions.

Description: Top or pyramid shaped, often covered with coralline algae. Some species with projecting spines on shell, giving a star-like outline. The interior is irridescent and the button-like operculum is thick and shelly. Commonly used for control of algae in aquariums.

Similar: *Trochus* and *Turbo.* spp.

Desirable/undesirable features: Useful in reef aquariums. Reef safe.

Food: Herbivorous. Filamentous algae, cyanobacteria and diatoms.

Special considerations: Hermit crabs may attack and kill them.

Hardiness in captivity: Growth and reproduction. Life span - months - years.

Astraea tecta congregate to spawn on "high ground" in a seagrass bed, Florida Keys.

Astraea tecta, left, *Turbo castanea*, right, and a rare hybrid cross between them, center.

Astraea caelata, left, *Astraea phoebia*, middle, and *Astrae tuber*, right. All occur in the Caribbean.

Astraea tecta from Florida. Sometimes specimens have projecting points at the shell margin.

Trochus

Common Name: Top Shell, Turban Shell

Region: Red Sea to Central Pacific

Description: Top or pyramid shaped, often covered with coralline algae but the markings are typically dark red stripes on a pale background. The interior is irridescent and the operculum is made of a horn-like proteinaceous material. Commonly used for control of algae in aquariums.

Similar: *Astraea*, *Turbo*, *Tectus*, and other Turban shells.

Desirable/undesirable features: Useful in reef aquariums. Reef safe.

Food: Herbivorous. Filamentous algae, cyanobacteria and diatoms.

Special considerations: Some species grow very large.

Hardiness in captivity: Growth and reproduction. Life span - months - years.

Trochus sp. in a dealer's aquarium.

Trochus erythraeus from the Red Sea. This is a very good herbivore in reef aquariums.

Trochus cf. *radiatus* from Oceanopolis, Brest, France reproduce prolifically in a reef display there.

Tectus fenestratus raised in aquaculture for the aquarium trade. House of Fins, Connecticut.

Stomatella

Common Name: Abalone, Limpet, Horse-ear

Region: Circumtropical.

Description: Shaped like an abalone, but more closely related to turban snails, this hitch-hiker on live rock and corals from the Western Pacific reproduces in reef aquaria, and is a desirable herbivore. When alarmed by a predator it can shed the tip of its meaty foot, like a lizard shedding its tail.

Similar: Abalones of the genus *Haliotis* are often confused with *Stomatella*. A shell-less nerite called *Titiscania limacina* from the Indo-Pacific region is similar to *Stomatella*.

Desirable/undesirable features: Useful in reef aquariums. Reef safe.

Food: Herbivorous. Filamentous algae, cyanobacteria and diatoms.

Special considerations: None.

Hardiness in captivity: Growth and reproduction. Life span - months - years.

Haliotis

Common Name: Abalone

Region: Circumtropical and temperate seas.

Description: Ear-shaped shell with irridescent interior and small breathing holes for exhaling water. Mantle with numerous projecting sensory antennae.

Similar: *Stomatella*

Desirable/undesirable features: Useful in reef aquariums. Reef safe.

Food: Herbivorous. Filamentous algae, cyanobacteria and diatoms.

Special considerations: Cool temperature for Eastern Pacific specimens. May starve in aquaria with short supply of algae. Offer dried seaweed (Nori) if the rocks are bare. Use extreme caution when removing from rocks or glass! Easily injured by careless handling.

Hardiness in captivity: So-so. Life span - months - years. Tropical species not reported to reproduce in aquaria.

Stomatella varia from Indonesia. Aquarium photo, Corallarium. Rome, Italy.

This small relative of *Stomatella* reproduces in aquariums. It is a harmless nocturnal herbivore.

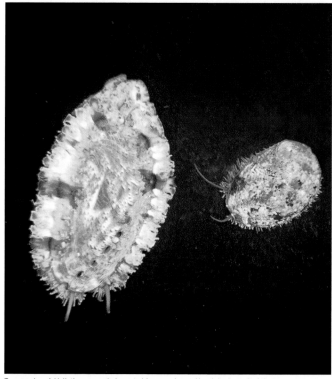

Two species of *Haliotis* commonly imported for aquariums. *H. asinina* is on the left.

Nerita

Common Name: Nerite

Region: Circumtropical

Description: Small rounded shells, smooth or with ridges. Common intertidally on rocky shores, in tidepools, on mudflats around mangroves, and on seagrasses. Herbivorous. Some species, such as *Nerita peloronta* from the Caribbean live at the water mark and crawl out of water to breathe. Such species are unsuitable for most home aquariums, unless a tidal system is employed. Other species are excellent in aquariums, being long-lived herbivores. Some species occur in brackish water and a few in freshwater.

Similar: There are several related genera of nerites, including the spectacular *Puperita pupa* from the Caribbean, and the similarly ornate and variable *Neritina*, *Neritodryas*, and *Theodoxus* spp. The author does not know why the latter four genera are separated, as variably colored individual specimens of any of them could be mistaken for the same species.

Desirable/undesirable features: Ornamental. Useful in reef aquariums. Reef safe.

Food: Herbivorous. Filamentous algae, cyanobacteria and diatoms.

Special considerations: Some species are intertidal and will crawl out of the aquarium.

Hardiness in captivity: Good. Nerites frequently lay eggs that look like sesame seeds, but no one has reported successful reproduction in aquaria. Life span - months - years.

Nerita sp. from Eilat, Israel. Red Sea. Ideal herbivores for a marine aquarium.

Nerita sp. in a tide pool, Virginia Key, Florida. Note sesame-seed-like eggs.

The natural habitat of *Neritina virginica*. Miami, Florida.

The Zebra Nerite, *Puperita pupa* left and center, is a beauty from the Caribbean. Nerita sp., right.

Norrisia

Common Name: Norris Top Shell, Red Foot or Mexican Red Foot Snail

Region: Central California to Western Mexico

Description: Reddish mantle is distinctive. This is a temperate water snail collected in Baja California among kelp weeds. Prefers water temperatures below 80 degrees Fahrenheit.

Similar: *Tegula* and *Gaza* spp.

Desirable/undesirable features: Useful in reef aquariums. Reef safe.

Food: Herbivorous. Filamentous algae, cyanobacteria and diatoms.

Special considerations: Temperature. These snails are harvested from cooler waters and do not permanently tolerate temperatures above 74 degrees Fahrenheit. May starve in aquaria with inadequate supply of fleshy algae. Offer dried seaweed (Nori) as food if the rocks are bare.

Hardiness in captivity: Poor. Life span weeks - months.

The Mexican Red Foot Snail is not long-lived in tropical aquariums.

Nassarius

Common Name: Nassa Snail

Region: Coastal zone of most Oceans.

Description: Small snail with an appearance like an olive pit. Has a long trunk-like siphon. Common on sand and mudflats or in seagrass beds. Useful "clean-up crew" in aquariums because they eat fish waste or decaying matter. They also burrow in the sand and help to keep it well aerated.

Similar: Most species are rounded, but some elongate ones may be confused with Ceriths. *Niotha, Phos, Reticunassa*, and *Telasco* spp. are very similar-looking relatives of *Nassarius*.

Desirable/undesirable features: Useful in reef aquariums. Reef safe.

Food: Carnivorous. Detritivore. Omnivore.

Special considerations: Maintain in an aquarium with a deep sand bed. Likes to burrow in sand.

Hardiness in captivity: Hardy but reproduction not reported. Life span - months - years.

Nassarius spp. are good scavengers of the bottom substrate. House of Fins, Connecticut.

Cerithium

Common Name: Cerith

Region: Circumtropical and some temperate regions.

Description: Ceriths are small shallow water spire-shaped snails that often live in huge aggregations of thousands of individuals on sandy or muddy bottoms. Some *Cerithium* spp. live on rocks on coral reefs. They feed on algae and detritus.

Similar: *Bittium, Batillaria, Terebralia, Rhinoclavis, Pseudovertagus, Clypeomorus.*

Desirable/undesirable features: Useful in reef aquariums. Reef safe.

Food: Herbivorous. Detritivore. Feeds on diatoms, cyanobacteria.

Special considerations: Hermit crabs may attack and kill them.

Hardiness in captivity: Growth and reproduction. Life span - months - years.

Ceriths from Florida.

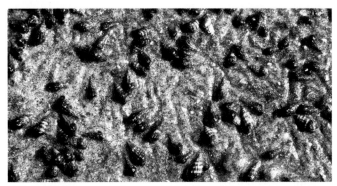

Batillaria spp. live in huge congregations on sand flats, feeding on detritus and algae.

Pusiostoma

Common Name: Bumble Bee Snail

Region: Western Pacific

Description: *Pusiostoma (=Engina) mendicaria* is a distinctive small snail with yellowish bands on a dark brown background, making it look like the abdomen of a bee. It occurs in rocky tide pools and is a hardy omnivore.

Similar: *Nassarius* spp., *Zeuxis (= Engina) zonalis, Enzinopsis lineata,*

Desirable/undesirable features: Ornamental. Useful in reef aquariums. Reef safe.

Food: Carnivorous. Detritivore. Omnivore.

Special considerations: Maintain in an aquarium with a deep sand bed. Likes to burrow in sand.

Hardiness in captivity: Hardy but reproduction not reported. Life span - months - years.

The Bumble Bee Snail is a popular scavenger for marine aquariums.

Heliacus

Common Name: Sundial

Region: Indo-Pacific, Red Sea?

Description: Small button shaped shell. Feeds on colonial zoanthids, particularly *Protopalythoa* spp. These snails are destructive and should be removed from the aquarium if one wants to grow zoanthids. In aquariums for stony corals, proliferating colonies of zoanthids may compete with corals. The zoanthids could be controlled with the sundial snail.

Similar: None

Desirable/undesirable features: Harmful to zoanthids. Possibly useful for reducing zoanthid populations. Reef safe (except for zoanthids).

Food: *Protopalythoa* and *Zoanthus* spp.

Special considerations: must have zoanthids to survive more than a few months in captivity.

Hardiness in captivity: Hardy. Life span - years when zoanthids present.

Heliacus variegatus found on a *Protopalythoa* sp. from Indonesia.

Fasciolaria

Common Name: Tulip Snail

Region: Caribbean, Atlantic, Gulf of Mexico, Brazil.

Description: Smooth banded snail with distinctive shape. Grows rather large, to approximately 10 inches. Beware: This snail feeds on *Astrea, Turbo,* and other snails. Therefore do not put it in a reef aquarium. It is a hardy and interesting snail in a fish aquarium. It will feed on chopped clam, mussel, and other meaty foods.

Similar: None.

Desirable/undesirable features: Ornamental. Not reef safe.

Food: Carnivorous. Feeds on snails and mollusk meat.

Special considerations: Feed mollusk meat.

Hardiness in captivity: Very hardy but reproduction not reported. Life span - years.

The tulip snail, *Fasciolaria tulipa* feeds on other snails, with a preference for *Turbo* and *Astraea* spp.

Strombus

Common Name: Conch

Region: Circumtropical and in Temperate regions

Description: *Strombus gigas*, the Queen Conch, is available as small tank raised specimens that are good herbivores. They clean and aerate the substrate as they burrow through it. They grow to enormous size, however, and may run out of food. Other smaller conchs are superb sand sifters and detritivores.

Similar: Numerous smaller species in this genus are suitable for reef aquariums or fish aquariums. Caution: some fishes will attack and eat conchs.

Desirable/undesirable features: Useful in reef aquariums. Reef safe.

Food: Herbivore. Detritivore.

Special considerations: *Strombus gigas* may starve in aquaria if the rocks are bare. Offer dried seaweed (Nori) as food. Maintain with sand.

Hardiness in captivity: Hardy. Life span - years.

Juvenile Queen Conch, *Strombus gigas,* produced by Oceans Reefs and Aquariums, Ft. Pierce, FL.

Juvenile Fighting Conch, *Strombus alatus* are excellent sand-cleaners. Harbor Branch. T. Smoyer.

Euplica

Common Name: Dove Shell

Region: Circumtropical

Description: Shell shaped like a dove. Small, to approximately 3/4 inch maximum size, cream colored, with brown markings. *Euplica* (=*Pyrene*) *versicolor* from the Indo-Pacific is a desirable herbivore that reproduces prolifically in reef aquariums. Pass this one on to friends!

Similar: The family Columbellidae contains other dove-shaped genera, including *Pyrene, Strombina, Columbella, Anachis, Parametaria, Mitrella, Dentimitrella, Microcitharia.* Several distantly related genera have similar shaped shells, including *Strombus, Mitra, Marginella.,* and *Pisania* spp.

Desirable/undesirable features: Useful in reef aquariums. Reef safe.

Food: Herbivore. Detritivore.

Special considerations: None.

Hardiness in captivity: Reproduces. Life span - years.

Euplica versicolor is a small herbivorous snail that reproduces prolifically in aquariums.

Cyphoma

Common Name: Flamingo Tongue

Region: Caribbean

Description: Mantle with pinkish or brown spots or dark stripes. Feeds on gorgonians. Should not be harvested because it is destructive in reef aquariums and quickly starves if not fed gorgonians, its only source of food.

Similar: Cowries and many ovulid snail species

Desirable/undesirable features: Ornamental. Not reef safe. Destructive or harmful to gorgonians.

Food: Carnivore. Feeds on specific types of gorgonians only.

Special considerations: Maintain in an aquarium with live gorgonians of the genus *Plexaurella* (favorite), *Pseudopterogorgia*, *Muricea*, or *Eunicea*, which must be sacrificed to keep this species alive.

Hardiness in captivity: Poor. Life span - weeks unless given natural diet.

Cyphoma gibbosum, left and *C. signatum*, right, feeding on a *Eunicea* sp. gorgonian.

Cyphoma macgintyi, an uncommon Flamingo Tongue.

Cyprea

Common Name: Cowries

Region: Circumtropical

Description: Egg-shaped glossy shell is typical of cowries, but also of the related Ovulids. Mantle extends from a slit -like opening and completely covers the shell. Cowries are mainly herbivores, but some feed on sponges or other invertebrates.

Similar: Ovulids

Desirable/undesirable features: Ornamental. Useful in reef aquariums. Reef safe. Small herbivorous species are desirable reef aquarium inhabitants. Large species are messy.

Food: Herbivorous. Carnivorous (some).

Special considerations: Large specimens can be very messy as they move about, knocking over corals and spreading copious mucus on the surfaces they tread. Large specimens may not get enough food. Offer dried seaweed (Nori) as food if the rocks are bare.

Hardiness in captivity: Hardy. Life span - years.

Cypraea tigris is a common, hardy cowrie, but not ideal in a reef aquarium.

Erosaria annulus, an excellent small herbivore.

Cypraea cervus, the Atlantic Deer Cowrie.

110

***Dendropoma*, *Serpulorbis*,** and other Genera

Common Name: Worm Shell, Vermetid snail

Region: All oceans

Description: Sessile snails that build a calcareous tube like some polychaete worms do. Most produce a "flag" or strings of mucus to trap food from the passing water or adjacent substrate. Some feed like clams by generating water currents to carry food past filter-feeding gills. Commonly imbedded in coral, sponges or attached to live rock.

Similar: The shells are often mistaken for worm tubes.

Desirable/undesirable features: Ornamental. Reef Safe.

Food: Filter feeder.

Special considerations: Must have sufficient calcium and alkalinity to build its tube dwelling. Supplemental additions of dissolved organic food and phytoplankton required for larger specimens.

Hardiness in captivity: Growth and reproduction. Life span - years

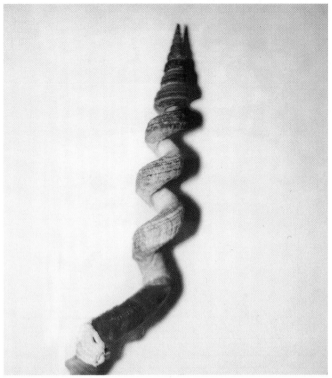

A vermetid snail, *Vermicularia* sp. from the Caribbean.

Vermetid snails in a tide pool, Virginia Key, Florida. They feed with mucus nets.

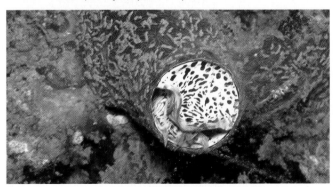

Serpulorbis grandis feeds on plankton that it seives from the water like a clam does.

Scutus

Common Name: Elephant snail, Scutus, Black Limpet

Region: Indo-Pacific

Description: *Scutus* cf. *unguis* is a fascinating limpet with its black umbrella-like mantel and curious antennae that wave up and down, touching the substrate as it slips along. It is a good herbivore in marine aquariums and reproduces prolifically. It mainly feeds on algae, but also eats tissue from hard and soft corals, so it cannot safely be housed in a live coral aquarium. There are several described species in the Pacific, and the common black one from Indonesia may or may not be *S. unguis*.

Similar: A beautiful keyhole limpet from the Caribbean with an orange mantle, *Lucapina aegis*, is very similar in appearance but not closely related to *Scutus*. It also will eat coral tissue, and so should not be housed with corals.

Desirable/undesirable features: Useful in marine aquariums without live corals. Not reef safe.

Food: Herbivorous. Filamentous algae, cyanobacteria and diatoms. Also feeds on coral tissue.

Special considerations: None.

Hardiness in captivity: Growth and reproduction. Life span - years.

Scutus cf. *unguis* is easily mistaken for a seaslug until the shell is revealed.

Scutus cf. *unguis* is a good herbivore that reproduces in aquaria. Unfortunately it eats live corals too!

113

Diodora

Common Name: Keyhole Limpet

Region: Circumtropical

Description: The apex of the shell has a hole. These pyramid shaped mollusks are excellent herbivores. They may also feed on the tissues of small polyped stony corals and soft corals. Harmless to large polyped stony corals. Some species may feed on the plague hydroid *Myrionema*. Several species reproduce in aquariums.

Similar: There are several genera of Keyhole limpets that have similar shells but quite different looking mantels.

Desirable/undesirable features: Useful in marine aquariums without small polyped stony corals. Reef safe.

Food: Herbivorous. Filamentous algae, cyanobacteria and diatoms. Also feeds on coral tissue and hydroids.

Special considerations: None.

Hardiness in captivity: Growth and reproduction. Life span - years.

Diodora sp. Florida.

The Keyhole Limpet *Lucapina aegis* feeding on *Acropora* tissue in an aquarium.

Diodora feeding on *Pocillopora damicornis.*

114

Cellana

Common Name: Limpet

Region: Circumtropical (there are many temperate and cold water species as well)

Description: Normally intertidal limpets that crawl above the water level periodically to breathe. At least one species remains below the water level and is suitable for aquariums.

Similar: *Acmaea* and *Patelloida*. The different species of these genera and *Cellana* spp. all look very similar.

Desirable/undesirable features: Useful in Reef aquariums. Reef safe.

Food: Herbivorous. Filamentous algae, cyanobacteria and diatoms.

Special considerations: Lives near water surface. Populations remain on glass (or aquarium walls) near the water surface.

Hardiness in captivity: Growth and reproduction. Life span - years.

The limpet *Cellana* resembles the barnacles around it. Virginia Key, Florida.

Cellana sp. that multiplies in aquariums, living on the aquarium walls just below the water line.

Chiton, Cryptoplax and Stenoplax

Common Name: Chiton

Region: All seas

Description: Specialized mollusks with eight articulating plates imbeded in a thick, tough mantle called a girdle. Chitons adhere tightly to rocks. Intertidal and subtidal. Active at night.

Similar: Similar to limpets, but distinguished by the eight plates. *Cryptoplax* species have a mantle that covers and thus conceals these plates.

Desirable/undesirable features: Useful in Reef aquariums. Reef safe in most cases.

Food: Herbivorous. Filamentous algae, cyanobacteria and diatoms. Some species reported to feed on coral tissue.

Special considerations: Intertidal species are not suitable for the average aquarium as they will crawl out of the water and out of the aquarium.

Hardiness in captivity: Hardy, Some very small species reproduce prolifically in aquariums. Life span - years.

Stenoplax floridana, the Florida slender chiton, here feeding on algae on the glass below the gravel.

A *Chiton* sp. feeding on the film of algae on the aquarium glass. Paris, France.

A tiny *Chiton* sp. that reproduces prolifically in reef aquariums, on live rock and in gravel.

Cryptoplax larvaeformis from the Indo-Pacific region has reduced plates and a thick girdle.

Tridacna

Common Name: Giant Clam

Region: Red Sea, Indian, and Pacific Oceans

Description: Conspicuous clams facing upward to receive light on their extended mantle that contains symbiotic zooxanthellae. Mantle in shades of blue, gold, green, or purple, with ornate patterns. Shells may have scales called "flutes."

Similar: *Hippopus* spp.

Desirable/undesirable features: Ornamental. Useful in reef aquariums. Reef safe.

Food: Filter feeder. Photosynthetic. Consumes dissolved organic substances and inorganic nutrients (ammonia, nitrate).

Special considerations: Light of sufficient intensity. Provide secure base for attachment, and protection of byssus opening. Use caution acclimating- sensitive to changes in specific gravity. Quarantine to prevent introduction of parasitic pyramidellid snails and protozoan disease (*Perkinsia*). May be attacked by certain polychaete worms.

Hardiness in captivity: Giant clams are farm raised commercially, but not reproduced by hobbyists. Life span - years. The hardiest species is *T. derasa*. The least hardy species is *T. crocea*, which requires very strong illumination.

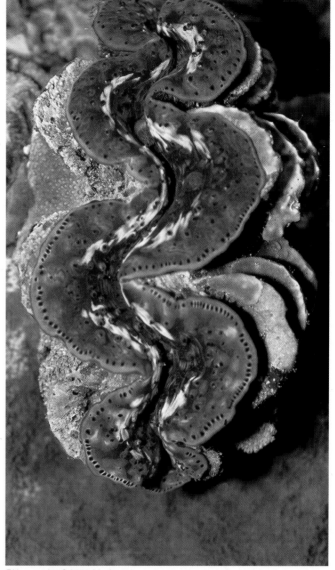

Tridacna maxima. Solomon Islands.

Closeup photo of the mantle of *Hippopus hippopus*, Solomon Islands.

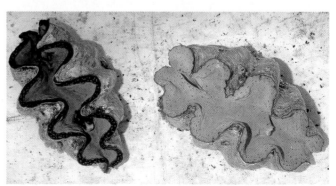

Tridacna gigas at the Giant Clam hatchery near Honiara, Solomon Islands.

Tridacna maxima specimens from the Red Sea can be especially blue.

Tridacna maxima with "Zebra" pattern. Solomon Islands.

This *Tridacna maxima* has a shell with wide-spaced scutes, like *T. squamosa*.

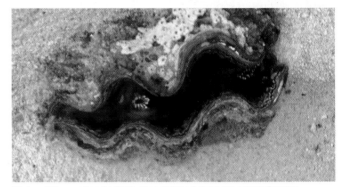

This large *Tridacna* sp. from the Red Sea has a shell like *T. derasa*. It is probably *T. maxima*.

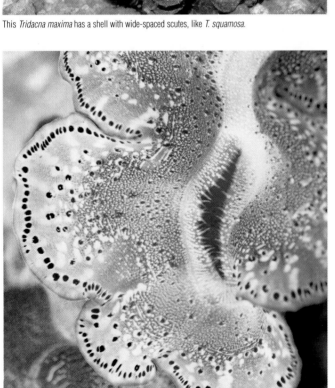

Tridacna maxima with metallic silver-blue mantle.

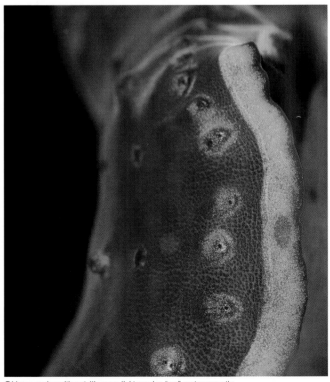

Tridacna maxima with metallic green light-sensing "eye" spots on mantle.

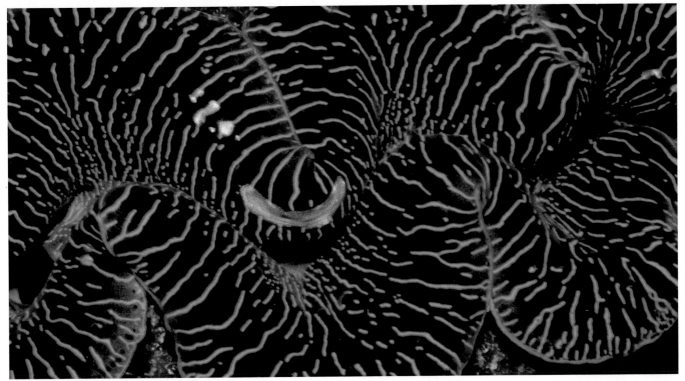

Tridacna maxima with blue "Zebra" pattern. Solomon Islands.

Tridacna maxima with a "Leopard" pattern. Solomon Islands.

Tridacna maxima. This color pattern is rare and among the most spectacular. Solomon Islands.

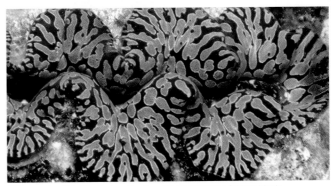

Tridacna maxima. This "Tiger" color pattern is common in Fiji and the Solomon Islands.

121

Tridacna crocea with a paisley pattern.

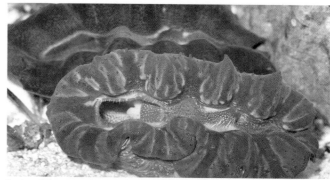

Two large *Tridacna crocea* in an aquarium. Normally they do not exceed 8 inches in shell length.

Tridacna crocea. Aquarium photo.

Tridacna crocea in its natural habitat: bored into the skeleton of a large coral head. Solomon Islands.

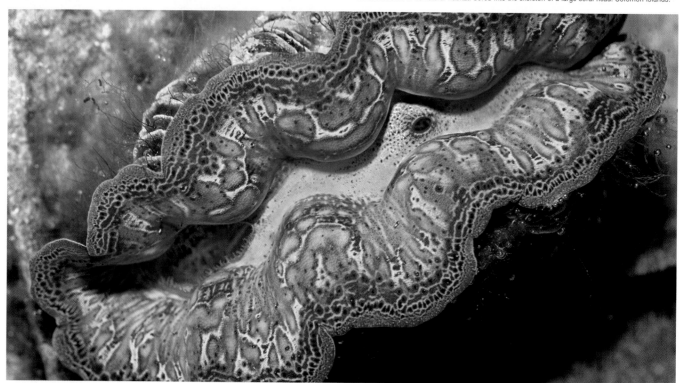

Tridacna crocea at the Giant Clam hatchery near Honiara, Solomon Islands.

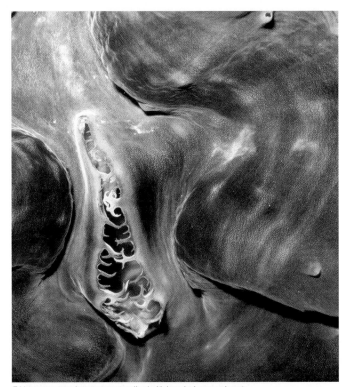

Tridacna squamosa incurrent aperture lined with branched sensory lappets.

A hybrid cross of *T. squamosa* and *T. maxima* produced in an aquaculture facility.

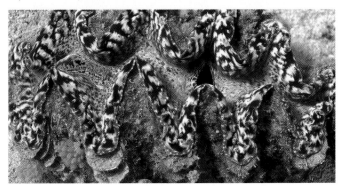

Red Sea *Tridacna* sp. with sharply margined shell, and mantle like T. squamosa. *T. rosewateri*?

Tridacna squamosa, typical coloration.

Tridacna squamosa.

123

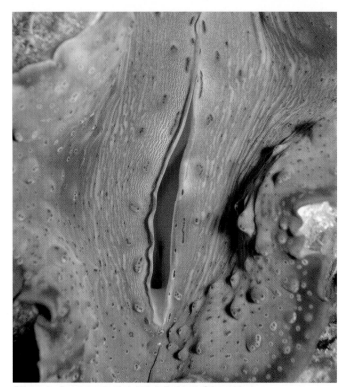

Tridacna gigas incurrent aperture lacks tentacle-like lappets. Solomon Islands.

Tridacna gigas, bright gold variety.

The author observes a large Tridacna gigas. Solomon Islands. Jeff Macare.

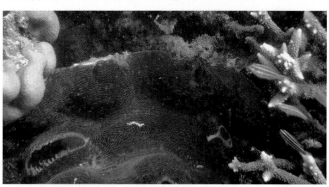

A blue striped adult Tridacna derasa on the Great Barrier Reef, Australia.

Tridacna derasa form with clear, round windows in mantle. Easily confused with T. gigas.

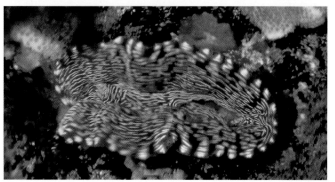

Tridacna derasa.

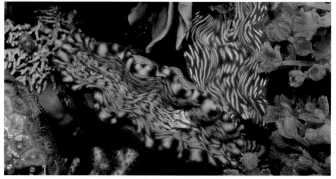

Tridacna derasa. Forms from different regions have distinct markings.

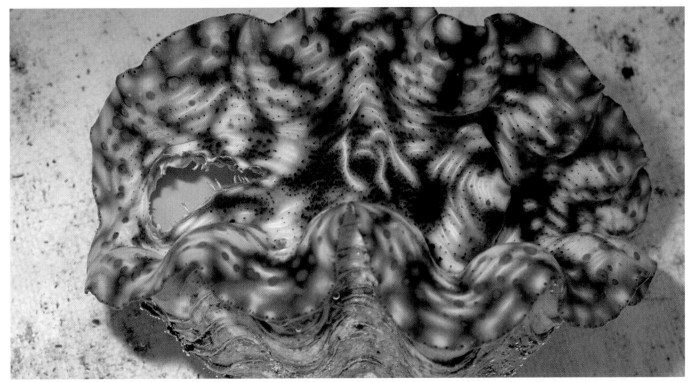

Tridacna derasa at the Giant Clam hatchery near Honiara, Solomon Islands.

Hippopus

Common Name: Horse's Hoof Clam, China Clam

Region: Western Pacific

Description: Triangular shell with thick ribs in *H. hippopus*, smooth shell in *H. porcellanus*. Cryptic colored mantle with symbiotic zooxanthellae does not extend beyond the margin of the shell aperture. Occurs on shallow reef flats.

Similar: Tridacna spp. clams.

Desirable/undesirable features: Ornamental. Useful in reef aquariums. Reef safe.

Food: Filter feeder. Photosynthetic. Consumes dissolved organic substances and inorganic nutrients (ammonia, nitrate).

Special considerations: Light of sufficient intensity. Use caution acclimating. Quarantine to prevent introduction of parasitic snails and protozoan disease (*Perkinsia*). May be attacked by certain polychaete worms.

Hardiness in captivity: Hardy. *H. hippopus* are farm raised commercially. Life span - years.

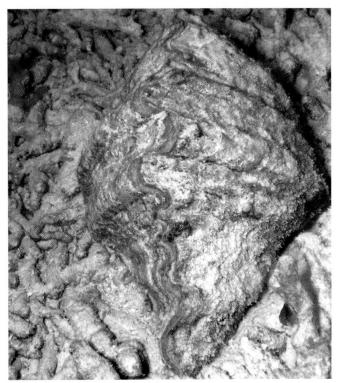

Hippopus hippopus, Solomon Islands.

Spondylus

Common Name: Thorny Oyster

Region: Circumtropical

Description: Large sessile clams with colorful mantles. Shell with spines or ridges. Cryptic on reefs and shipwrecks.

Similar: The shape of the shell is much like scallops, but *Spondylus* spp. remain firmly attached to the substrate and do not wander. *Pedum spondyloideum* is a colorful relative that lives within coral heads, normally boulder shaped *Porites* spp.

Desirable/undesirable features: Ornamental. Reef safe.

Food: Filter feeder. Dissolved and particulate organic substances (marine snow), bacteria and phytoplankton.

Special considerations: Daily food additions. Strong currents. Sensitive to changes in specific gravity. Quarantine to prevent introduction of protozoan disease. May be attacked by polychaete worms. Provide calcium and alkalinity for growth.

Hardiness in captivity: Poor. Life span - months - years (with care).

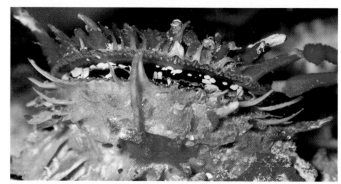
The thorny oyster, *Spondyllus americanus,* from the Caribbean.

Spondyllus varians has sensitive blue eyes along the margin of the mantle.

Spondyllus varians, Solomon Islands. The mantle is reminiscent of the aposematic colored flatworms.

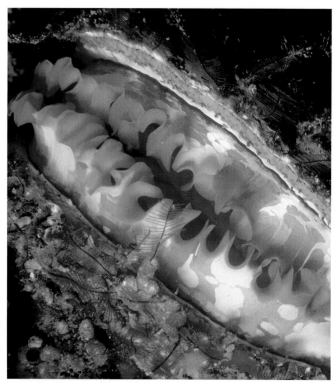
A happy *Spondyllus varians,* Solomon Islands.

Pedum spondyloideum, lives in live corals and has an outrageously colorful mantle. Solomon Islands.

Lima

Common Name: Flame Scallop, File shell clam

Region: Caribbean, Indo-Pacific

Description: "Flame Scallops" have fine bumps on the shells that make them feel like files, orange or white eye-lash-like tentacles, and red lip-like mantle flaps. A species from the Indo-Pacific has a thin region on the "lips" that seems to light up like a small electric arc. The effect is produced by a flap of tissue that rapidly covers and uncovers a bright blue-white stripe. *Lima lima*, a small species from the Caribbean has a purple mantle and tentacles. The long lash-like tentacles of *Lima* spp. are sensory, but also trap and transfer drifting "marine snow" particles to the mantle

Similar: Scallops of the genus *Pecten*. *Limaria* and *Promantellum* spp. are similar to Lima, but have sticky tentacles that may be used for prey capture or predator deterrance.

Desirable/undesirable features: Ornamental. Reef safe.

Food: Filter feeder. Dissolved and particulate organic substances ("marine snow"), bacteria and phytoplankton.

Special considerations: Provide sufficient food. Provide sufficient calcium and alkalinity for growth.

Hardiness in captivity: Poor. Life span - months - years (with care). Recent attention to the use of phytoplankton and organic foods (marine snow) has produced much better success with *Lima* spp. than was previously realized.

Lima sp. the Flashing Flame Scallop has a white margin on the mantle that flashes like an electric arc.

Lima scabra, the Flame Scallop.

Sometimes *Lima scabra* has white tentacles.

Lima cf. *pellucida*. Living Seas Aquarium, Chicago.

127

Pycnodonta and *Lopha*

Common Name: Cock's Comb Oyster, Cats Paw

Region: Red Sea to Central Pacific

Description: Jagged tooth-like margin to the shell aperture. *Pycnodonta* is larger and more heavily calcified than *Lopha*.

Similar: *Dendostrea* from the Caribbean was formerly classified in the genus *Lopha*.

Desirable/undesirable features: Ornamental. Reef safe.

Food: Filter feeder. Dissolved and particulate organic substances (marine snow), bacteria and phytoplankton.

Special considerations: Provide sufficient food (dissolved and particulate organics, phytoplankton). Provide strong currents. Use caution acclimating- sensitive to changes in specific gravity. Quarantine to prevent introduction of parasitic snails and protozoan disease (*Perkinsia*). May be attacked by certain polychaete worms.

Hardiness in captivity: Poor.
Life span - months - years (with care).

Arca

Common Name: Turkey Wing, Ark Clam

Region: Circumtropical and in temperate regions

Description: Wing-shaped clam, attached to hard substrates and often covered by encrusting algae and other marinelife. Commonly introduced into aquariums with live rock. Several species of Turkey Wing shells, when cleaned, are colored like a slice of vanilla ice-cream with chocolate stripes.

Similar: *Barbatia* and *Andara* spp.

Desirable/undesirable features: Ornamental. Reef safe.

Food: Filter feeder. Dissolved and particulate organic substances (marine snow), bacteria and phytoplankton.

Special considerations: Provide sufficient food (dissolved and particulate organics, phytoplankton). Provide strong currents. Use caution acclimating- sensitive to changes in specific gravity. May be attacked by certain polychaete worms.

Hardiness in captivity: Hardy. Life span - years.

Pycnodonta (=*Hyotissa*) *hyotis*. Solomon Islands.

Lopha cristagalli. Solomon Islands.

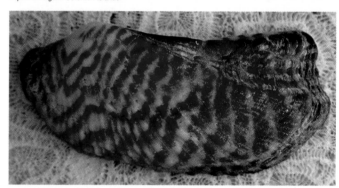

Arca sp. Turkey Wing shell.

Arca imbricata attached to live rock, Florida.

128

Pinna

Common Name: Pen Shell

Region: Circumtropical

Description: Fan-shaped oyster partially buried in sand or mud, on seagrass beds or sometimes imbedded in rock on reefs. They usually occur in strong tidal water flow, which assists them in obtaining their food.

Similar: *Atrina* spp.

Desirable/undesirable features: Ornamental. Reef safe.

Food: Filter feeder. Dissolved and particulate organic substances (marine snow), bacteria and phytoplankton.

Special considerations: Provide sufficient food (dissolved and particulate organics, phytoplankton), strong water flow, calcium and alkalinity for growth. Put pointed end in sand.

Hardiness in captivity: Poor. Life span - weeks. Recent attention to the use of phytoplankton and organic foods (marine snow) has produced only marginally better success with *Pinna* spp. than was previously realized.

Pinna carnea, the Amber Pen Shell, is translucent. Other Pen Shells are thicker. It is not hardy.

Perna

Common Name: Blue-Lipped Mussel, Green Mussel.

Region: All oceans, brackish and some freshwater habitats.

Description: Elongate flattened green mussel with bright blue-green margins.

Similar: Other genera of mussels including *Septifer, Mytilus, Modiolus, Crenomytilus,* and *Hormomya.*

Desirable/undesirable features: Ornamental. Reef safe.

Food: Filter feeder. Dissolved and particulate organic substances (marine snow), bacteria and phytoplankton.

Special considerations: Provide sufficient food. Provide sufficient calcium and alkalinity for growth.

Hardiness in captivity: Poor. Life span - months. *Perna viridis*, is not very long-lived in aquariums. Recent attention to the use of phytoplankton and organic foods (marine snow) has produced better success with *Perna* than was previously realized. Some mussels can be long-lived or even reproduce in aquaria, but many starve and die within months.

The black siphon contrasts with the brilliant blue-green shell.

Octopus

Common Name: Octopus

Region: Red Sea, Indian and Pacific Oceans

Description: Eight armed intelligent masters of disguise and color transformation, with suction cups lining the undersides of the arms.

Similar: Squids and cuttlefish

Desirable/undesirable features: Ornamental. Useful in reef aquariums*. Toxic to people*. Harmful to fishes. Harmful to crustaceans. Reef safe.

Food: Carnivorous. Feeds on shrimps and crabs. *Sometimes employed in reef aquariums on a temporary basis for the eradication of stomatopods (mantis shrimps).

Special considerations: Harmed by pump intakes or overflow drains. Will crawl through minute openings (because they have no bones) and escape from the aquarium. Therefore octopuses require specially designed aquariums to prevent their escape. Public aquariums put artificial grass carpeting around the aquarium border to prevent escape. Apparently *Octopus* species are repelled by the texture. Some species of *Octopus* have a dangerous bite.

Hardiness in captivity: Poor. Only with special care are these magnificent creatures possible to maintain for their natural life span. Most are not long-lived, with a natural life span of approximately one to two years.

Hapalochlaena lunulata is lovely but deadly. It should not be imported. Max Gibbs.

The common day-active reef octopus, *Octopus cyanea*, from the Indo-Pacific. Solomon Islands.

131

Sepia

Common Name: Cuttlefish

Region: Red Sea, Indian and Pacific Oceans, Mediterranean

Description: Squid-like cephalopods distinguished by the presence of a cuttle bone (internal calcium carbonate wedge) and a fin along the full body length.

Similar: Squids and Octopus.

Desirable/undesirable features: Ornamental. Harmful to fishes and crustaceans. Reef safe.

Food: Carnivorous. Feeds on shrimps and crabs.

Special considerations: Temperature for subtropical species. Harmed by pump intakes or overflow drains. Aquarium size-some species grow large and need a large aquarium to accomodate them. Best kept in a display for cuttlefish only, with rock decoration for shelter.

Hardiness in captivity: Growth and reproduction. Life span - months. Fast growing but life span is not much more than one or two years, depending on species.

Among the most intelligent invertebrates is this proud Giant Cuttlefish, *Sepia latimanus.*

Metasepia pfefferi, the Flamboyant Cuttlefish, is a spectacular a creature, but very delicate. Bruce Carlson, Waikiki Aquarium.

132

Nautilus

Common Name: Chambered Nautilus

Region: Indian and Pacific Oceans

Description: The only cephalopods with an external shell. *Nautilus pompilius* is the species most commonly encountered. Specimens entering the aquarium trade usually originate from the Philippines. *Nautilus* species are found from 60 to 750 meters depth, the shallower range being reached generally at night only, when they migrate to shallower depths to feed. These creatures require special aquariums with chilled water (65 degrees F). These creatures should not be housed in a tropical brightly illuminated reef aquarium!

Similar: Several species of *Nautilus* exist, and a new genus was recently erected for one of them.

Desirable/undesirable features: Ornamental. Reef safe*.

Food: Carnivorous. Feeds on crabs and shrimps.

Special considerations: Temperature. Nautilus live in cool water and do not tolerate tropical temperatures! Light: Nautilus come from deepwater where the light is spectrally blue and not very bright. They do not tolerate the conditions found in shallow reefs and are thus not suitable for the typical reef aquarium. *A deepwater chilled reef display (with black corals, *Tubastraea*, and other non-photosynthetic species) could house *Nautilus*. Diet: Feed whole crabs, including the shell. Calcium: maintain high alkalinity for proper shell growth.

Hardiness in captivity: Growth as well as reproduction has been achieved at some public aquariums.
Life span - months - years.

Nautilus pompilius. Solomon Islands.

Tank-raised *Nautilus* hatched at the Waikiki Aquarium. Bruce Carlson.

A bucket full of *Nautilus pompilius* collected in the Solomon Islands.

Worms

The segmented worms belong to the phylum Annelida, which includes the familiar earthworm and many aquatic species. The marine habitat has a tremendous array of annelids, in the water; on and inside rocks, corals, sponges and other invertebrates; on the surface of sand and mud, burrowed in soft substrates; and in tubes constructed of organic material, calcium carbonate, or fused sand grains. Some annelids are parasites (leeches, for instance), but most subsist on organic material and bacteria sorted from the substrate or filtered from the water. Some species are carnivores, such as the fireworms, *Hermodice* and *Eurythoe*, well known to aquarists.

Annelids include approximately 9000 described species, in three distinct classes: Polychaeta, Oligochaeta, and Hirundinea. Most marine species are in the class Polychaeta, freshwater and terrestrial annelids are mostly Oligochaeta, and Hirundinea are leeches.

All annelids are vermiform (worm-shaped, like a spaghetti noodle), though the addition of tentacles, hair-like setae, and scales may so alter their outline that the worm shape is no longer obvious. In addition, some tube dwelling species have dramatically modified segments used for water pumping or burrowing, and the filter-feeding feather duster worms produce fantastic flower-like crowns of feathery appendages.

Another feature of annelid worms is metamerism, the division of the body into segments arranged in a linear series. This feature is shared with arthropods, to which annelid worms are related.

Marine aquariums contain many species of worms, introduced with living rock and sand substrates. While a few species are problematic predators, most are beneficial processors of organic detritus and substrate aerators. There are also a few ornamental species harvested for aquariums.

Sabellastarte

Common Name: Giant Feather Duster

Region: Indo-Pacific, Caribbean

Description: Large tentacular crown, up to more than six inches in diameter, but typically about four inches. A pair of ventral collar lobes below the crown deposits the sediment and organic matrix tube in which the worm dwells.

Similar: Small brown or dull orange specimens of *Sabellastarte* may be confused with large similarly colored specimens of *Bispira*.

Desirable/undesirable features: Ornamental. Reef safe.

Food: Filter feeder. Bacteria, particulate organic matter.

Special considerations: These subsist mainly on bacteria and organic matter produced within the aquarium, but benefit from supplemental feeding of phytoplankton and liquid organic foods.

Hardiness in captivity: Growth and reproduction. Life span - months - years.

Sabellastarte sp. Solomon Islands.

This feather duster on a deep reef slope in the Red Sea has fluorescent orange pigment in its crown.

Sabellastarte sp. from Singapore, Kenny Tan.

Unidentified feather duster worm, possibly a *Sabellastarte* species, from Japan.

Bispira

Common Name: Cluster Duster, Feather Duster

Region: Caribbean, Mediterranean, and Indo Pacific

Description: Crown usually purplish or bluish-white, but may also be brown or dull orange, often bicolored or with patterns. The tube is soft smooth and gray, composed of deposited detritus. The common *Bispira* cf. *viola* multiplies by fission readily in the aquarium, forming dense colonies in the shade. "Cluster Dusters" *Bispira brunnea* from the Caribbean do not survive well in aquariums unless collected with hard substrate and maintained without predatory fishes or serpent stars, that quickly devour them.

Similar: *Branchiomma* sp

Desirable/undesirable features: Ornamental. Reef safe.

Food: Filter feeder. Bacteria, particulate organic matter.

Special considerations: These subsist mainly on bacteria and organic matter produced within the aquarium, but benefit from supplemental feeding of phytoplankton and liquid organic foods.

Hardiness in captivity: Growth and reproduction. Life span - months - years, except *Bispira brunnea*, see above.

Bispira brunnea the "Cluster Duster" from the Caribbean does not thrive in aquariums.

This *Bispira* sp. from Singapore is hardy and beautiful. A great species for novice aquarists. K. Tan.

Bispira sp. from Indonesia in the aquarium of Doug Robbins.

Bispira variegata from the Caribbean catches particulate material and uses it to construct its tube.

137

Notaulax

Common Name: Feather Duster

Region: Indo-Pacific, Caribbean

Description: The parchment-like tube is located within a hole in live rock, usually on the underside of a ledge. Only the crown emerges. The crown is very sensitive to motion and withdraws quickly.

Similar: *Anamobaea* spp., which have a visible tube.

Desirable/undesirable features: Ornamental. Reef safe.

Food: Filter feeder. Bacteria, particulate organic matter.

Special considerations: These subsist mainly on bacteria and organic matter produced within the aquarium, but benefit from supplemental feeding of phytoplankton and liquid organic foods.

Hardiness in captivity: Hardy, but reproduction not reported. Life span - years.

Notaulax occidentalis lives in live rock and disappears in the blink of an eye.

Salmacina and *Filogranella*

Common Name: Red hard-tube duster rock.

Region: Circumtropical

Description: Clusters of white calcareous tubes of approximately 1mm in diameter or less, with red or white crowns.

Similar: *Vermiliopsis*

Desirable/undesirable features: Ornamental. Reef safe.

Food: Filter feeder. Bacteria, particulate organic matter.

Special considerations: These subsist mainly on bacteria and organic matter produced within the aquarium, but benefit from supplemental feeding of phytoplankton and liquid organic foods. Need sufficient calcium and alkalinity for growth of tubes.

Hardiness in captivity: Growth and reproduction. Life span - months - years

Salmacina sp. Solomon Islands.

Filogranella sp. from Florida. Photographed in the author's aquarium by Alf J. Nilsen.

Protula

Common Name: Hard Tube Duster, Coco Worm

Region: Indo-Pacific

Description: A hard calcareous tube approximately 1/2 inch (12 mm) in diameter at the opening from which the crown emerges, and tapering toward the rear end. The tube is often mostly straight, about five to eight inches long, and coiled at the distal end. The crown may be white, orange, red, yellow, or patterned with these colors. Older crowns are spiraled. Newly grown crowns are bi-lobed.

Similar: When imbedded in live coral *Protula* may be confused with *Spirobranchus*.

Desirable/undesirable features: Ornamental. Reef safe.

Food: Filter feeder. Bacteria, particulate organic matter.

Special considerations: These subsist mainly on bacteria and organic matter produced within the aquarium, but benefit from supplemental feeding of phytoplankton and liquid organic foods. Need sufficient calcium and alkalinity for growth of tubes. Prefer moderately strong water currents.

Hardiness in captivity: Fair. Life span - months - years (with care).

Red *Protula bispiralis*, the "Hard Tube Feather Duster" from Singapore, Kenny Tan.

Protula bispiralis from Singapore with a well developed double crown, Kenny Tan.

Protula bispiralis from Indonesia, sifting food from the moderate currents they prefer. Aquarium photo.

Spirobranchus

Common Name: Christmas Tree Worm. Jewel Stone.

Region: Circumtropical

Description: Crown spiraled in the shape of a Christmas tree. Collected in Indonesia. Harvest involves collection of coral, usually *Porites* sp., which requires CITES permit.

Similar: *Protula*

Desirable/undesirable features: Ornamental. Reef safe.

Food: Filter feeder. Bacteria, particulate organic matter.

Special considerations: These subsist mainly on bacteria and organic matter produced within the aquarium, but benefit from supplemental feeding of phytoplankton and liquid organic foods. Need sufficient calcium and alkalinity for growth of tubes. Prefer moderately strong water currents.

Hardiness in captivity: Fair.
Life span - months - years (with care).

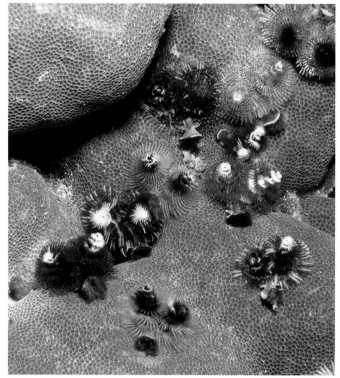

Spirobranchus spp. Solomon Islands.

Spirobranchus spp. often occur in large, multi-colored aggregations, usually on heads of the stony coral *Porites*.

Timarete

Common Name: Ball of Yarn Worm

Region: Circumtropical

Description: Orange, reddish, or brownish small burrowing worm with two anterior clusters of grooved hair-like dorsal tentacles that it uses to feed on detritus particles in the sediment where it lives. Commonly observed in aquariums in the gravel adjacent to viewing windows. Also common in live rock. Family Cirratulidae. Various snails and seaslugs eat them.

Similar: Terebellid or "Spaghetti" worms.

Desirable/undesirable features: Useful in reef aquariums.

Food: Deposit feeder. Bacteria, particulate organic matter from the bottom and within live rocks.

Special considerations: Provide sand or gravel bottom material to encourage them to populate the aquarium.

Hardiness in captivity: Growth and reproduction.
Life span - years.

The Ball of Yarn Worm is a useful sandbed and live rock resident. It comes free with live rock.

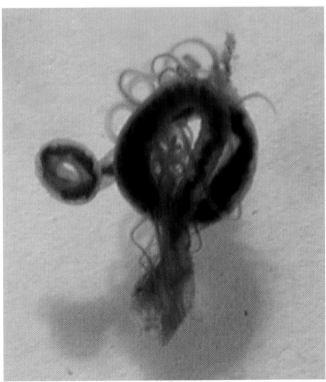

Timarete sp. Note the dark detritus inside its gut cavity.

141

Eupolymnia, *Loimia*, and *Reteterebella*

Common Name: Spaghetti Worm.

Region: Indo-Pacific, Caribbean.

Description: Spaghetti-like tentacles extend over the substrate to gather detritus and associated microfauna. The food passes along a groove in the tentacles as if on a conveyor belt. These worms live in a tube made of secreted organic material with sand and gravel cemented on the outside, either buried in the substrate or under rocks.

Similar: *Timarete* (family Cirratulidae), and *Phyllochaetopterus* (family Chaetopteridae)

Desirable/undesirable features: Ornamental. Useful in reef aquariums.

Food: Deposit feeder. Bacteria, particulate organic matter.

Special considerations: Provide sand or gravel bottom material to encourage them to populate the aquarium.

Hardiness in captivity: Growth and reproduction (by fission usually). Life span - months - years.

Reteterebella queenslandia. Solomon Islands.

Eupolymnia crassicornis removed from its tube located on the underside of a rock. Key Biscayne, Florida.

Chapter Six

Hermodice and *Eurythoe*

Common Name: Fire Worm, Bristle Worm

Region: Caribbean and Indo-Pacific

Description: Dorso-ventrally flattened with lateral rows of needle-like often venomous bristles. Contact with skin causes extreme burning sensation and swelling. *Hermodice carunculata* grows to 40 cm. Either genus may feed on hard and soft corals and anemones, or may injure or eat small tridacnid clams placed directly on sand. Small *Eurythoe* spp. are detritivores and do not harm most sessile invertebrates.

Similar: Other polychaete worms.

Desirable/undesirable features: Destructive or harmful to corals and tridacnid clams. Toxic to people. Not reef safe, except for some smaller species, which are detritivores.

Food: Omnivore, scavanger, carnivore. Cnidarian tissues.

Special considerations: None.

Hardiness in captivity: Growth and reproduction. Life span - years.

Large numbers of small *Eurythoe* spp. may develop in sand and under live rocks. They are scavengers.

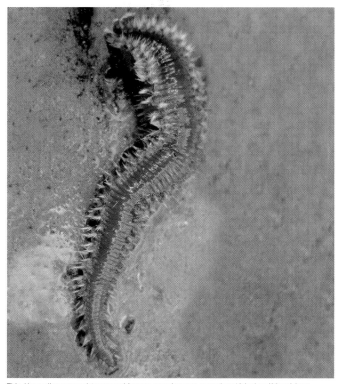

This *Hermodice carunculata* removed from an aquarium was more than 12 inches (30 cm) long.

Hermodice carunculata feeding on a gorgonian. Note the missing tissue on the branch tip.

143

Arthropods

rthropods are invertebrates with jointed legs and a stiff or hard exoskeleton. They include crabs, shrimps, lobsters, hermit crabs, barnacles, amphipods, ostracods, copepods, and isopods, beetles, wasps, butterflies and other insects, centipedes, millipedes, daddy-longlegs, spiders, scorpions, sea-spiders, and horseshoe crabs, among other things with lots of legs and antennae. Eighty-five percent of all animals are members of this very diverse and successful group.

The seas are full of arthropods, from the plankton to deep sea bottom habitats, and they have most successfully invaded the land as well. More than 750,000 species are described.

Arthropods are quite similar to annelid worms in many respects. Most are segmented and have paired appendages, though in some (crabs, for example) the segments have become reduced. The arthropods and annelids also share similar nervous system architecture. The chief distinguishing characteristic of arthropods is their chitinous exoskeleton or "cuticle." The exoskeleton is divided into plates that cover each segment, and they articulate by means of a flexible articular membrane that connects them.

This chapter features the arthropods that are popular among aquarists, including shrimps, lobsters, crabs and hermit crabs, plus some other interesting but less conspicuous members of this group that often find their way into aquariums.

This group is among the most popular, full of fantastically shaped and colored animals that also happen to be very durable aquarium inhabitants for the most part. Herbivorous arthropods are also utilized in aquariums for their algae grazing capacity, and some shrimps are the best known control for pesky *Aiptasia* anemones. Furthermore, a variety of shrimps provide a "cleaning service" for fishes on the reef, picking off parasites at well advertised cleaning stations. The talents of these creatures is a product of their numerous sensitive legs, which seem to be able to smell and taste in addition to feel and grab! The advertisement for this service is accomplished with improbable gaudy colors and dancing or antennae waving, a real spectacle on the reef or in an aquarium!

Neopetrolisthes*, *Porcellana* and *Petrolisthes

Common Name: Porcelain Crabs

Region: Circumtropical

Description: Flattened carapace and claws, and large modified maxillipeds used to gather planktonic food. *Neopetrolisthes oshimai* and *N. maculatus* are commensals on *Stichodactyla* spp. sea anemones, and may also eat mucus. *Petrolisthes* spp. are filter feeders, but eat scraps of food as well. They live in and underneath live rocks. *Porcellana sayana* occurs inside live Conch shells or with hermit crabs.

Similar: Similar to *Galathea* spp. (Squat Lobsters).

Desirable/undesirable features: Ornamental. Reef safe.

Food: Carnivorous. Filter feeder.

Special considerations: All porcelain crabs actively feed on particulate organic matter drifting in the water. Offer liquid foods and chopped meaty food particles.

Hardiness in captivity: Hardy Life span - years.

Neopetrolisthes maculatus has a finer pattern of red spots than *N. oshimai* has.

Petrolisthes sp. from the Caribbean. Note the feather-like chelipeds used for gathering food.

A pair of *Porcellana sayana* in the opening of the shell of a large hermit crab.

Neopetrolisthes oshimai occurs on sea anemones, usually in pairs.

Percnon

Common Name: Sally Lightfoot, Spray Crab

Region: Circumtropical

Description: *Percnon gibbesi* is the common Sally Lightfoot collected for aquariums. It is dark brown or maroon with yellow rings on the legs and a fine yellow line on the face, but becomes less colorful as it grows large. The carapace is very flattened, which assists in its ability to slip quickly between rocks.

Similar: *Plagusia* and *Grapsus spp.*

Desirable/undesirable features: Ornamental. Useful in reef aquariums. Harmful to fishes. Reef safe.

Food: Herbivorous. Good for algae control. Carnivorous. Large specimens may catch and eat small fishes.

Special considerations: None.

Hardiness in captivity: Hardy. Life span - years.

The Sally Lightfoot crab, *Percnon gibbesi.*

Percnon gibbesi has a very flattened body with bright yellow spots on the legs that break up its outline. It is a good herbivore but dangerous to small fishes.

147

Stenorhynchus

Common Name: Arrow Crab, Spider Crab

Region: West and East Atlantic, Eastern Pacific, Mediterranean?

Description: *Stenorhynchus seticornis* is the common arrow crab from the Caribbean, where it occurs under ledges on reefs and rocky outcroppings. *Stenorhynchus lanceolatus* from the east Atlantic and *S. debilis* from the eastern Pacific have stockier bodies but are colored similarly.

Similar: *Eplumra phalangium* (Western Pacific) is practically identical. *Chirostylus dolichopus* from the Western Pacific lacks the long rostrum, but has essentially the same appearance.

Desirable/undesirable features: Ornamental. Harmful to fishes. Reef safe.

Food: Carnivorous.

Special considerations: Large specimens may catch and eat small fishes. May eat bristle worms.

Hardiness in captivity: Hardy. Life span - years.

The Arrow Crab, *Stenorhynchus seticornis*, is a real character, hardy, and long-lived.

This *Chirostylus* sp. spider crab from Japan looks like an arrow crab but lacks the long rostrum.

Leptopisa

Common Name: Spider Crab, Decorator Crab

Region: Caribbean,

Description: Spider-like, with small legs and large triangular carapace. Rostrum is short and forked. Places pieces of sponge, algae, etc. on its carapace to camouflage its outline.

Similar: *Macrocoeloma* and *Cyclocoeloma* spp.

Desirable/undesirable features: Ornamental. Harmful to some invertebrates. Harmful to fishes. Reef safe.

Food: Omninivorous. Algae, detritus, fish waste, decomposing dead animal or vegetable matter. Large specimens may catch and eat small fishes.

Special considerations: Their activity of placing bits of sponge, algae, zoanthid polyps, soft corals, etc. on their carapace for camouflage means that they may harm the creatures they trim for their decoration. In a large aquarium their activity helps spread and propagate the species they trim.

Hardiness in captivity: Hardy. Life span - years.

Leptopisa setirostris both damages and helps to spread the creatures it uses for decoration.

This *Leptopisa setirostri s* covered with sponge is almost invisible on a mangrove root.

Camposcia

Common Name: Spider Crab, Decorator Crab

Region: Red Sea, Indo-Pacific

Description: *Camposcia retusa* Very spider-like, with large legs and small carapace. Rostrum is short and forked. This crab places pieces of sponge, algae, detritus, etc. on its carapace and legs to camouflage its outline.

Similar: Other decorator crabs cover themselves similarly. *Pelia* spp. from the Caribbean are similar, but much smaller.

Desirable/undesirable features: Ornamental. Harmful to some invertebrates. Not reef safe.

Food: Carnivorous. Chopped fish, clams, other meaty foods.

Special considerations: Their activity of placing bits of sponge, algae, zoanthid polyps, soft corals, etc. on their carapace for camouflage means that they may harm the creatures they trim for their decoration. In a large aquarium their activity helps spread and propagate the species they trim.

Hardiness in captivity: Hardy. Life span - years.

Mithraculus

Common Name: Emerald Crab, Spider Crab, Hardback Crab

Region: Caribbean, Atlantic

Description: *Mithraculus (=Mithrax) sculptus*, the Emerald Crab, has a shiny green carapace and furry legs, with spoon-shaped tips on the claws. It is a superb algae eater, used in aquaria to control bubble algae (*Ventricaria* and *Valonia* spp.). *M. cincinctimanus* has banded purplish legs and associates with anemones and corals and *M. forceps*, which is brown or orange, occurs with the Emerald crab.

Similar: *Trapezia* and *Tetralia. Mithraculus* is a new genus recently distinguished from *Mithrax*. Memebers of the latter genus grow to substantially larger size.

Desirable/undesirable features: Useful in reef aquariums. Harmful to small fishes. Reef safe.

Food: Herbivorous. Carnivorous.

Special considerations: May catch and eat small fishes.

Hardiness in captivity: Hardy. Life span - years.

The spider crab *Camposcia retusa* decorates itself with bits of sponge and algae.

Mithraculus sculptus, the Emerald Crab from the Caribbean, is an attractive useful herbivore.

Mithraculus forceps (brown) and *M. sculptus* (green) are very similar.

149

Lybia

Common Name: Pom-Pom Crab, Boxer Crab

Region: Red Sea, Indian Ocean, Pacific

Description: Small crabs distinguished by habit of carrying the anemone *Bunodeopsis* sp. in each claw like a pair of boxing gloves, used for defense and feeding. *Lybia* wipes the anemones on the substrate and feeds on the material that adheres to them, arguably tool usage combined with mutualism. *Lybia tesselata* is the most common species collected for aquariums. *Lybia caestifera* is more cryptic and *L. edmondsoni* from Hawaii is similar to *L. tesselata*.

Similar: None

Desirable/undesirable features: Ornamental. Reef safe.

Food: Herbivorous. Carnivorous.

Special considerations: Keep in a small aquarium where they are easy to observe. Harmed by fishes that may try to eat them.

Hardiness in captivity: Hardy. Life span - years.

Lybia tesselata carries its "Pom-Pom" anemones, *Bunodeopsis* sp.

Calappa

Common Name: Shame-Faced Crab, Fountain Crab

Region: Circumtropical and temperate seas.

Description: The flattened modified claws are used to extract snails from their shells! Straughan, 1973 observed that when placed in a shallow dish of saltwater, the water currents *Calappa* passes over its gills are so strong as to form a fountain-like stream.

Similar: None

Desirable/undesirable features: Ornamental. Harmful to invertebrates. Harmful to fishes. Not reef safe.

Food: Herbivorous. Carnivorous. Snails. Also feeds on other meaty foods. Large specimens may catch and eat small fishes.

Special considerations: Not compatible with snails. Its digging habits make it a potential bulldozer. Best kept in an aquarium by itself with a sand or gravel substrate. Feed whole snails and watch how it pries them open!

Hardiness in captivity: Hardy. Life span - years.

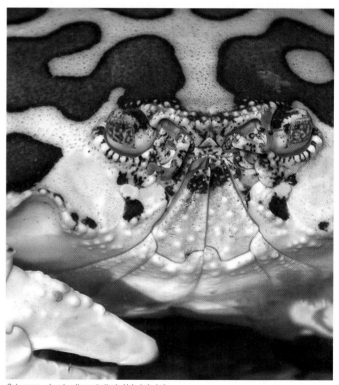

Calappa sp. planning its next attack. Heh, heh, heh.

Dromia

Common Name: Sponge Crab, Decorator Crab

Region: Circumtropical

Description: Roundish compact crabs that carry a partially excavated cap-shaped sponge or algal mass on their back, using modified legs to hold the object in place. *Dromia erythropus*

Similar: *Cryptodromiopsis, Leptopisa, Macrocoeloma, Hypoconcha*

Desirable/undesirable features: Harmful to some invertebrates. Not reef safe.

Food: Carnivorous. Chopped fish, clams, other meaty foods.

Special considerations: Their activity of placing bits of sponge, algae, zoanthid polyps, soft corals, etc. on their carapace for camouflage means that they may harm the creatures they trim for their decoration. In a large aquarium their activity helps spread and propagate the species they trim.

Hardiness in captivity: Hardy. Life span - years.

The sponge crab *Dromia* holds a cap-shaped sponge on its back with its specially modified hind legs.

Trapezia

Common Name: Coral Crabs

Region: Red Sea, Indian, and Pacific Oceans

Description: Flattened smooth shelled crabs that live between the branches of stony corals, particularly in *Acropora, Pocillopora, Seriatopora*, and *Stylophora* spp.

Similar: *Tetralia* and *Quadrella* spp.

Desirable/undesirable features: Ornamental. Reef safe.

Food: Carnivorous. Chopped fish, clams, other meaty foods. Also coral mucus.

Special considerations: These crabs live in live coral heads and may benefit from the mucus secretions of their host. Therefore the crab should be maintained with live *Acropora, Pocillopora, Seriatopora*, or *Stylophora* spp. Their host benefits because the crab wards off would-be predators.

Hardiness in captivity: Hardy. Life span - years.

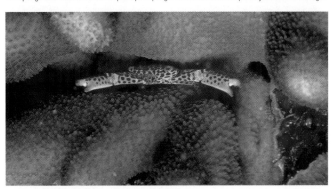

Trapezia living in *Stylophora pistillata*, Solomon Islands.

Trapezia sp. living in an *Acropora* sp., Aquarium photo, Paris, France.

151

Uca

Common Name: Fiddler Crabs

Region: Circumtropical

Description: Inhabitants of intertidal mudflats, especially around mangroves in the tropics, these small crabs live in holes dug in the muck. They form communities of hundreds or thousands, and the m ales wave their larger "fiddle" claw to communicate and attract mates.

Similar: None.

Desirable/undesirable features: Ornamental. Not reef safe.

Food: Omnivorous. Chopped fish, clams, other meaty foods, algae, seagrass, detritus.

Special considerations: Not suitable for the typical marine aquarium. Should only be maintained in a habitat that mimics the intertidal mudflat structurally. They must be able to crawl out of the water periodically onto a shore-like structure.

Hardiness in captivity: Hardy when maintained in the proper environment. Life span - years.

Uca spp. can spend time completely submerged, but need to crawl out of the water periodically.

Colorful *Uca* sp. crabs are hardy but not suiteable for typical aquariums.

Uca sp. with long eye-stalks.

The habitat where *Uca* spp. can be found: intertidal sand and mudflats among mangroves.

Ciliopagurus

Common Name: Striped Hermit Crab

Region: Red Sea to Hawaii.

Description: *Ciliopagurus* (=*Trizopagurus*) *strigatus* has a flattened carapace, an adaptation to its preference of living in cone shells that have a narrow, slit-like opening. The legs and claws are banded yellow and red. Claws with dark tips.

Similar: *Aniculus* spp., which grow larger and aren't flat.

Desirable/undesirable features: Ornamental. Not reef safe. Harmful to invertebrates. Harmful to small fishes.

Food: Omnivorous. Feed on filamentous algae and cyanobacteria, coral mucus, meaty foods.

Special considerations: May harm clams, feather duster worms, or other invertebrates. Large specimens are destructive in a reef aquarium. Otherwise hardy, charming pets. Safe with large fishes as long as those fishes don't feed on hermit crabs (as do trigger fish, puffer fish, some large wrasses).

Hardiness in captivity: Hardy. Life span - years.

Ciliopagurus strigatus seems to be a creature from the imagination of Dr. Seus. Marj Awai.

Aniculus

Common Name: Hairy Hermit Crab

Region: Pacific

Description: *Aniculus* spp. have bands on the legs and claws, and distinctive bristles. *Aniculus maximus* is among the most exquisite of all hermit crabs and commands a high price.

Similar: *Ciliopagurus strigatus*.

Desirable/undesirable features: Ornamental. Not reef safe. Harmful to invertebrates, small fishes, and small children!

Food: Omnivorous. Meaty foods.

Special considerations: Large specimens are destructive to everything in their path. Otherwise charming pets. Keep alone (with some live rock and gravel or sand), and provide adequate biological filtration and aeration. Sensitive to ammonia and low oxygen levels. Large powerful claws can cause painful injury to a finger. Keep away from children.

Hardiness in captivity: Hardy. Life span - years.

Aniculus aniculus is a common reef flat hermit crab from the Pacific.

Aniculus maximus from Hawaii.

Clibanarius

Common Name: Blue Leg Hermit, Hermit Crab

Region: Circumtropical

Description: *Clibanarius* spp. live in intertidal regions on rocky shores, in tide pools, and on seagrass and Mangroves. *Clibanarius tricolor*, the Blue Leg Hermit from the Caribbean is popularly used for the control of algae in reef aquaria.

Similar: Small specimens of *Calcinus* spp.

Desirable/undesirable features: Useful in reef aquariums. Reef safe.

Food: Herbivorous. Good for algae control. Feed on filamentous algae and cyanobacteria. Also carnivorous.

Special considerations: May attack and eat snails, taking their shell for a new residence. A large population of hermit crabs utilized for algae control may starve once they have reduced the quantity of algae. Offer them dried seaweed (Nori) or remove some and place them in other aquariums.

Hardiness in captivity: Hardy. Life span - years.

Paguristes

Common Name: Red Legged Hermit, Red Reef Hermit

Region: Caribbean

Description: *Paguristes cadenati* is the popular Red Legged Hermit utilized for control of filamentous algae in aquariums. It occurs most frequently on coral bommies on offshore reefs.

Similar: *Calcinus tibicen.*

Desirable/undesirable features: Useful in reef aquariums. Reef safe.

Food: Herbivorous. Good for algae control. Feed on filamentous algae and cyanobacteria. Also carnivorous.

Special considerations: May attack and eat snails, taking their shell for a new residence. A large population of hermit crabs utilized for algae control may starve once they have reduced the quantity of algae. Offer them dried seaweed (Nori) or remove some and place them in other aquariums.

Hardiness in captivity: Hardy. Life span - years.

Clibanarius sp. from the eastern Pacific.   A large *Clibanarius* sp. from Florida.

Clibanarius tricolor, the Blue-Legged Hermit.

Paguristes cadenati is very skilled at grazing filamentous algae between coral branches.

Phimochirus

Common Name: Polkadotted hermit

Region: Caribbean, Atlantic

Description: *Phimochirus operculatus* has orange legs, a polkadotted body, and a large white claw that it uses like an operculum when it withdraws into its shell. It is an extremely active species. *Phimochirus holthuisi* has striped brown and white legs and a large white claw.

Similar: *Manucomplanus* (=*Polypagurus*) *varians*

Desirable/undesirable features: Ornamental. Useful in reef aquariums. Reef safe.

Food: Herbivorous. Good for algae control. Feed on filamentous algae and cyanobacteria. Also carnivorous.

Special considerations: May attack and kill snails, eating them and taking their shell for a new residence. Members of this genus are territorial. Do not put more than one specimen in a small aquarium since they will fight until one of them dies.

Hardiness in captivity: Hardy. Life span - years.

Manucomplanus (=*Polypagurus*) *varians*

Common Name: Antler or Staghorn Hermit Crab

Region: Eastern Pacific

Description: *Manucomplanus* (=*Polypagurus*) *varians* has a special relationship with a hydroid named *Janaria mirabilis* that envelops the shell in which the hermit crab lives. The hydroid forms a calcareous skeleton with pointed "antlers," commonly mistaken for coral.

Similar: *Phimochirus* resembles *Manucomplanus*. In the Gulf of Mexico the bryozoan *Hippoporidra edax* envelops a shell occupied by a hermit crab, and then continues to grow in the same manner as *Janaria* does.

Desirable/undesirable features: Ornamental. Reef safe.

Food: Omnivorous. Offer meaty foods.

Special considerations: The hydroids require fine particulate food to thrive. They can be maintained with daily feeding of liquid food preparations for filter feeding invertebrates.

Hardiness in captivity: Hardy. Life span - years.

P. operculatus runs quickly but pulls into its shell and drops at the sign of danger. Greg Schiemer.

Phimochirus operculatus checks out a new shell for size. Greg Schiemer.

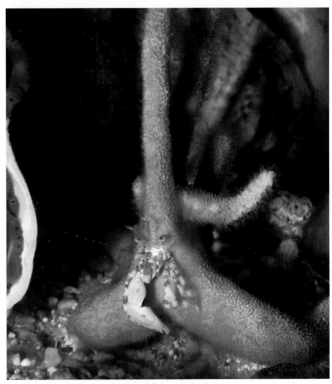

The staghorn hermit crab, *Manucomplanus* (=*Polypagurus*) *varians*.

Calcinus

Common Name: Red leg hermit, Blue knuckle hermit

Region: Circumtropical

Description: *Calcinus* species have unequal sized claws (the left is usually larger) and long eyestalks. They occur in tidepools and on reefs.

Similar: *Paguristes*.

Desirable/undesirable features: Useful in reef aquariums. Reef safe.

Food: Herbivorous. Good for algae control. Feed on filamentous algae and cyanobacteria. Also carnivorous.

Special considerations: Large specimens may attack and kill snails, eating them and taking their shell for a new residence. If a large population of hermit crabs is utilized for algae control, they may starve once they have reduced the quantity of algae. In that case offer them dried seaweed (Nori) or remove some and place them in other aquariums.

Hardiness in captivity: Hardy. Life span - years.

Dardanus

Common Name: Spotted Hermit Crab, Stareye Hermit

Region: Circumtropical and in temperate regions.

Description: Hairy legs and claws, unequal sized claws. *Dardanus megistos* is a darling red creature with white polkadots and a very active mind. One never knows what destructive mischief it will get into next.

Similar: Some large *Paguristes* spp. hermit crabs have similar hairy legs and claws of equal size.

Desirable/undesirable features: Ornamental. Not reef safe. Harmful to invertebrates. Harmful to fishes.

Food: Omnivorous. Feed on filamentous algae and cyanobacteria, anemones, snails, fishes, you name it.

Special considerations: Will eat just about anything they decide to pinch and mutilate. Destructive in a reef aquarium and dangerous to house with slow or sluggish fishes. Otherwise charming pets.

Hardiness in captivity: Hardy. Life span - years.

Calcinus laevimanus. Country Critters, NY.

The beautiful blue-knuckle hermit, *C. elegans*.

Calcinus californiensis. Greg Schiemer.

Calcinus tibicen. Greg Schiemer.

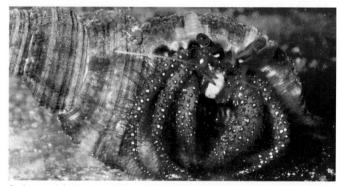

Dardanus megistios pauses to consider the meaning of life as it chews the remains of a tankmate.

Dardanus pedunculatus lives with commensal sea anemones.

158

Do not confuse the blue-jointed predator *Dardanus guttatus* shown above with the benign, blue--knuckled herbivore *Calcinus elegans* shown opposite it, on the left.

Paguritta

Common Name: Coral Hermit Crab

Region: Indo-Pacific

Description: Sessile. Living in holes in coral heads. Use long feather-like antennae to catch plankton. It is a treat to observe colonies of them feeding, looking like so many violinists in concert.

Similar: Resemble barnacles.

Desirable/undesirable features: Ornamental. Reef safe.

Food: Filter feeder. Carnivorous.

Special considerations: Provide liquid foods prepared for filter feeding invertebrates, and/or brine shrimp nauplii. Target feed small pieces of chopped shrimp. Harmed by certain fishes such as wrasses and some blunt-nosed hawkfishes, pufferfish, and triggerfish. Take care to keep the live coral host healthy by placing it in proper illumination and water flow, and providing proper calcium and alkalinity levels.

Hardiness in captivity: Hardy. Life span - years.

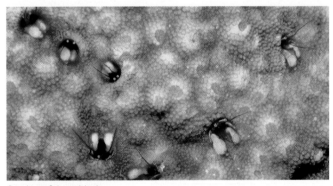

Paguritta sp. Solomon Islands.

Paguritta gracilipes. Solomon Islands.

159

Lepas

Common Name: Gooseneck Barnacle

Region: All seas.

Description: Attach to drifting objects in the open ocean and the hulls of sea-going boats. Commonly washed ashore. These stalked barnacles have a flexible "neck" and five white articulating plates that resemble the shells of a clam. They extend large reddish brown feeding appendages that trap zooplankton, phytoplankton and organic matter.

Similar: Look like bivalve clams.

Desirable/undesirable features: Ornamental. Reef safe.

Food: Filter feeder. Particulate organic matter. Zooplankton.

Special considerations: Provide liquid foods for filter feeding invertebrates, and/or rotifers and brine shrimp nauplii, or finely chopped shrimp. Harmed by certain fishes such as wrasses, hawkfishes, pufferfish, and triggerfish.

Hardiness in captivity: Poor. Life span - weeks. With regular feeding it may be possible to grow and reproduce them.

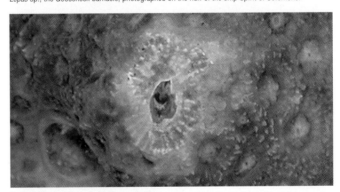

Lepas sp., the Gooseneck barnacle, photographed on the hull of the ship Spirit of Solomons.

Pyrgomatid Barnacles

Common Name: Coral Gall Barnacle

Region: Circumtopical

Description: These barnacles occur in cyst-like galls in coral skeletons. They bore into the skeleton and the coral continues to grow around them. The barnacle extends its feeding appendages from a slit or funnel-shaped opening.

Similar: Could be confused with the sessile hermit crab *Paguritta*.

Desirable/undesirable features: Ornamental. Reef safe.

Food: Filter feeder. Feeds on coral mucus and particulate organic matter.

Special considerations: Provide liquid foods prepared for filter feeding invertebrates, and/or rotifers and brine shrimp nauplii. Take care to keep the live coral host healthy by placing it in proper illumination and water flow, and providing proper calcium and alkalinity levels.

Hardiness in captivity: Hardy. Life span - years.

Coral Gall barnacle in a *Goniopora* sp. skeleton.

Coral Gall barnacle in *Euphyllia glabrescens*. J. C. Delbeek.

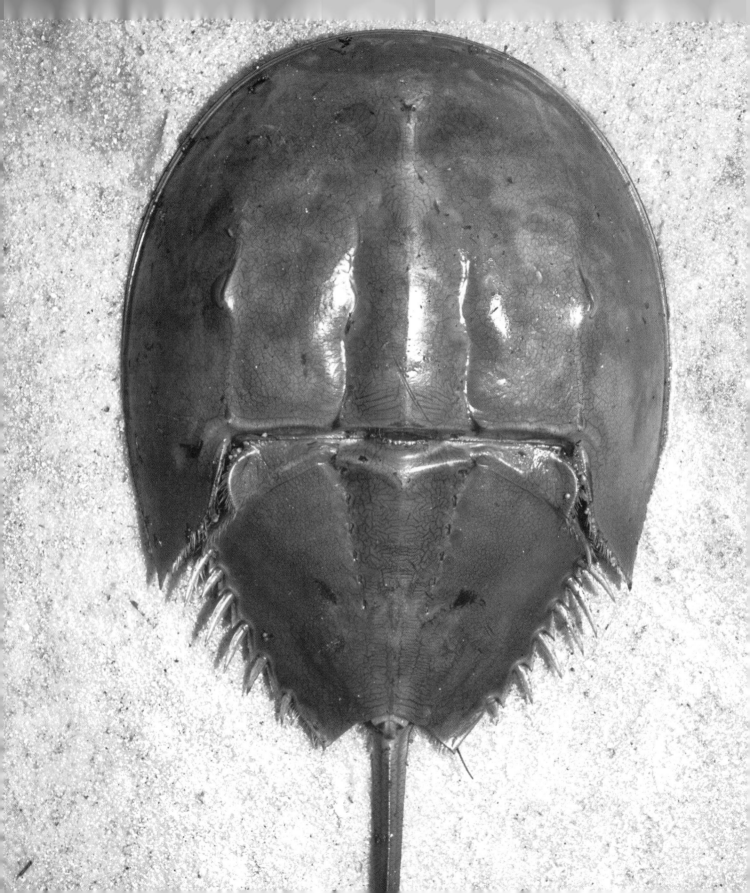

Limulus

Common Name: Horseshoe crab

Region: Atlantic coast of North America to Mexico and Central America. Other genera in Asia.

Description: Horseshoe crabs are not true crabs, but belong to a group known as chelicerates. They are most closely related to scorpions and spiders. Adult female horseshoe crabs can be 12 inches wide and 24 inches long. Males are smaller. The larvae look like Trilobites.

Similar: None

Desirable/undesirable features: Ornamental. Useful in reef aquariums*. Destructive or harmful to some invertebrates, especially worms or clams. Harmful to fishes. Reef safe.

Food: Scavenger. Omnivore.

Special considerations: Provide sand or gravel. *Small specimens are useful bottom cleaners, but eventually grow too large. Large specimens are destructive bulldozers.

Hardiness in captivity: Hardy. Life span- years.

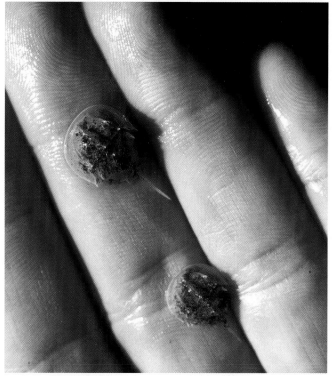

Juvenile *Limulus polyphemus.*

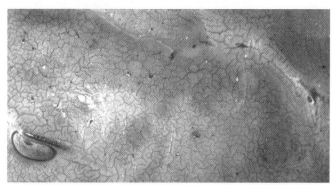

The eyes of *Limulus polyphemus* include large compound ones (Left) and smaller simple ones (right).

Juvenile *Limulus polyphemus* are used for cleaning sand bottoms in aquariums.

Lysmata and *Lysmatella*

Common Name: Peppermint Shrimps. Scarlet Cleaner.

Region: Caribbean, Atlantic, Mediterranean, Red Sea, Indian, Pacific

Description: Peppermint colored shrimps

Similar: *Parhippolyte* spp., *Rhynchocinetes* and *Cinetorhynchus*

Desirable/undesirable features: Ornamental. Useful in reef aquariums. Harmful to small tridacnid clams. Reef safe.

Food: Carnivorous. Scavenger, cleaner of parasites off fishes. Some species feed on *Aiptasia* anemones.

Special considerations: Acclimate newly acquired specimens slowly to the aquarium! They are extremely sensitive to changes in specific gravity and pH. Harmed by fishes such as groupers, Marine Betta (*Caloplesiops*), some wrasses, triggerfishes, large clownfishes.

Hardiness in captivity: Growth and reproduction. Life span - years.

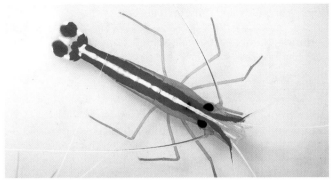

Lysmata amboinensis, the Scarlet Cleaner Shrimp, requires careful, slow acclimation.

Lysmata debelius, a popular and hardy aquarium resident.

Lysmata rathbunae is similar to *L. wurdemani*.

Lysmata wurdemani, the Peppermint Shrimp, is useful for controlling *Aiptasia* anemones.

Rhynchocinetes and *Cinetorhynchus*

Common Name: Peppermint Shrimp, Camel Shrimp, Hinge-Beak Shrimp

Region: Circumtropical

Description: Hump-backed shrimp with an upwardly angled rostrum and large eyes. The rostrum is hinged and movable. Typically colored in shades of red. Males are distinguished from females by their much larger claws. They live in crevices and caves on reefs.

Similar: *Lysmata* spp., *Saron* spp.

Desirable/undesirable features: Ornamental. Destructive or harmful to some corals. Reef safe.

Food: Carnivorous.

Special considerations: Harmed by fishes that might eat it, such as *Calloplesiops altivelis*. Provide cave structure for them and keep them in groups. Feed often with chopped meaty foods, worms, or flakefood.

Hardiness in captivity: Hardy. Life span - years.

Cinetorhynchus hiatti, Hiatt's Hinge-Beak Shrimp.

Cinetorhynchus hendersoni.

Rhynchocinetes durbanensis.

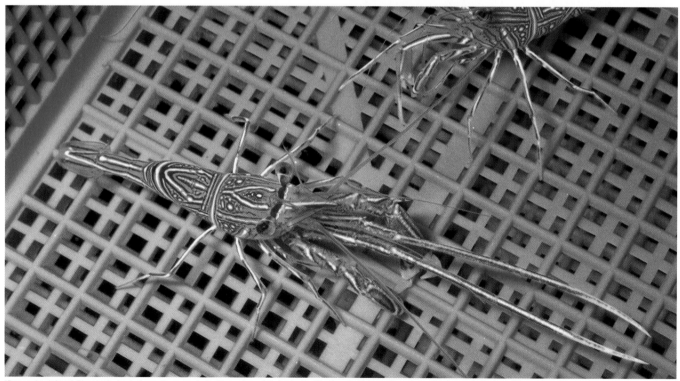

"Peppermint shrimps" *Rhynchocinetes durbanensis* are popular hardy aquarium pets but not safe with all corals. Male specimen, below, has longer chelipeds and bigger claws than female, above.

Saron

Common Name: Marble Shrimps

Region: Red Sea to Hawaii

Description: Cryptic coloration with patterns like polished marble. Adult males are distinguished by their larger claws. Some species have tufts of hair-like cirri dorsally and ventrally.

Similar: None

Desirable/undesirable features: Ornamental. Destructive or harmful to some corals and zoanthids. Harmful to other invertebrates. Not reef safe.

Food: Carnivorous.

Special considerations: Provide cave structure. Feed often with chopped meaty foods, worms, or flakefood. Can be maintained in a simple reef aquarium with live rocks and leather corals.

Hardiness in captivity: Hardy. Life span - years.

Saron inermis, male specimen.

Saron sp., male. This shrimp is probably a color form of the variable species *S. marmoratus.*

Saron rectirostris, the Purple-leg marble shrimp, female.

Saron marmoratus, the common marble shrimp, male specimen.

Saron sp. This shrimp is probably a color form of the variable species *S. marmoratus.*

Thor

Common Name: Sexy Shrimp

Region: Circumtropical

Description: *Thor amboinensis* is fascinating to observe as it struts along the tentacles of an anemone or coral, waving its abdomen up and down in a provocative manner. It is brown with white polkadots and blue markings. A real gem in a small reef aquarium!

Similar: *Hymenocera* and *Periclimenes* spp. have a polkadot pattern. *Gnathophyllum* spp. are small and colorful.

Desirable/undesirable features: Ornamental. Reef safe.

Food: Carnivorous. Chopped meaty foods, worms, flakefood.

Special considerations: Harmed by fishes that might eat it. Provide an anemone or large polyped coral (*Euphyllia*, *Plerogyra*, for example) and keep in groups. Keep in a small aquarium. Acclimate with care. Sensitive to changes in specific gravity and pH. Sensitive to low oxygen levels.

Hardiness in captivity: Delicate. Life span - years.

Gnathophyllum

Common Name: Bumble-Bee Shrimp

Region: Circumtropical and in Temperate seas.

Description: Small shrimps with stocky bodies and a squared off head. Patterns of stripes or spots. Look for them on the undersides of large flat rocks or under sea urchins.

Similar: *Thor* spp. are also small and colorful.

Desirable/undesirable features: Ornamental. May harm small sea urchins or small seastars by feeding on their tube feet. Reef safe.

Food: Carnivorous.

Special considerations: Harmed by fishes that might eat them. Territorial. Forms pairs and fights with other specimens. Feed often with finely chopped meaty foods, worms, or flakefood. Keep in a small aquarium. Acclimate with care. Sensitive to changes in specific gravity and pH. Sensitive to low oxygen levels.

Hardiness in captivity: Delicate. Life span months-years.

Thor amboinensis on *Megalactis hemprichii*, Solomon Islands.

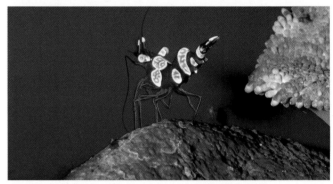

Thor amboinensis in a small "jewel box" aquarium. Aquarium at Kushimoto Japan.

Gnathophyllum sp. from Southern Australia. Carol Buchanan.

Unidentified *Gnathophyllum* sp. collected in the Gulf of Mexico by Dave Smith. Rob and Robin Burr.

Hymenocera

Common Name: Harlequin Shrimp

Region: Red Sea, Indo Pacific to Eastern Pacific.

Description: Shaped and colored like an orchid bloom, these small shrimps feed exclusively on seastars. Two species are described, *H. picta* from the Eastern Pacific to central Pacific, including Hawaii, and *H. elegans* from the Western Pacific, Indian, and Red Sea. The latter is whitish or pale yellow with pink-centered purplish blue spots. The former is white with pinkish or yellow rimmed reddish spots. The distinction between the species on the basis of color is a subject of debate. It may be that one species only exists, *H. picta*, which was described first.

Similar: Some *Periclimenes* spp. are colored with similar markings, especially *P. colemani*.

Desirable/undesirable features: Ornamental. Harmful to sea stars. Reef safe.

Food: Carnivorous. Feeds on the arms and tube feet of seastars. It may be possible to maintain them in an aquarium with a large population of the small, vegetatively reproducing seastars *Asterina* spp. (Mitch Gibbs, pers. comm.).

Special considerations: Harmed by fishes that might eat it, such as *Calloplesiops altivelis*, wrasses, and hawkfishes. Territorial. Forms pairs. Special diet: must be supplied with seastars to eat. Only requires one feeding per month to survive, but can be fed more often. Best maintained and observed in a small aquarium. Acclimate with care. Sensitive to changes in specific gravity and pH. Sensitive to low oxygen levels.

Hardiness in captivity: Hardy. Has been raised in a captive aquaculture project at the Waikiki aquarium. Life span - years.

Hymenocera picta in the reef aquarium of David Saxby, London.

Hymenocera elegans at Reef International, Milan, Italy.

Periclimenes

Common Name: Pederson's Shrimp, Anemone Shrimp, Pepperoni Shrimp, Cleaner Shrimp

Region: Circumtropical and in temperate seas.

Description: Colorful shrimps commonly associated with anemones, cerianthids, corallimorphs, and corals, but also associated with echinoderms.

Similar: *Pilopontonia, Vir, Urocaridella,* Allopontonia, and *Hamopontonia.*

Desirable/undesirable features: Ornamental. Reef safe.

Food: Carnivorous. Also feeds on mucus from its host. In extreme starvation it may feed on the tentacles of anemones.

Special considerations: Harmed by fishes that might eat it, such as *Calloplesiops altivelis*, wrasses, and hawkfishes. Forms pairs. Keep in a small aquarium. Harmed by pump intakes or overflow drains. Acclimate with care. Sensitive to changes in specific gravity and pH. Sensitive to low oxygen levels.

Hardiness in captivity: Hardy. Life span - years.

Periclimenes sp., Solomon Islands.

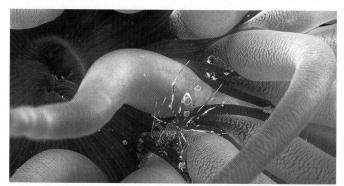

Periclimenes yucatanicus, Puerto Rico.

Urocaridella sp., Solomon Islands.

Periclimenes brevicarpalis in an Aquarium in Paris, France.

170

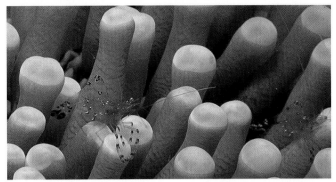

Periclimenes cf. *tosaensis* on the mushroom coral, *Heliofungia actiniformis.* Solomon Islands.

Periclimenes kororensis, Solomon Islands.

Periclimenes rathbunae, Puerto Rico.

Periclimenes cf. *tosaensis* on the tube of a cerianthid. Solomon Islands.

Allopontonia iaini, a relative of *Periclimenes,* is associated with the sea urchin *Asthenosoma varium.*

Stenopus

Common Name: Boxer Shrimp, Banded Coral Shrimp, Coral Banded Shrimp

Region: Circumtropical.

Description: elongated claws and legs, and long hair-like antennae. Most clean parasites from fishes. An undescribed species from deep water in the Gulf of Mexico and Brazil has a color pattern like *Stenopus spinosus* from the Mediterranean.

Similar: *Microprosthema* spp. *Odontozona* sp.

Desirable/undesirable features: Ornamental. Useful in reef aquariums. Reef safe. Feeds on small bristle worms.

Food: Carnivorous. Will take most meaty foods.

Special considerations: Harmed by fishes that might eat it, such as Groupers, *Calloplesiops*, hogfish, triggerfish, and hawkfishes. Memebers of this genus occur singly or in pairs, and aggressively attack others of their kind. Purchase known pairs or house single individuals only. Acclimate with care.

Hardiness in captivity: Hardy. Life span - years.

Stenopus hispidus.

Stenopus scutellatus in an aquarium.

Unidentified *Stenopus* sp. from the Gulf of Mexico, eating a bristle worm in an aquarium.

Stenopus pyrsonatus.

172

Alpheus and *Synalpheus*

Common Name: Pistol or Snapping Shrimp

Region: Circumtropical and in temperate seas.

Description: Shaped like a Maine lobster, often colorful. One of the claws has a "hammer" capable of producing very audible sound. It is used for defense and prey capture, and also for boring tunnels in coral. Often live in holes in the sand, sometimes with a symbiotic "partner goby." Some are commensal on sponges, anemones, corals, or echinoderms).

Similar: *Coralliocaris* spp., which associate with stony corals, particularly *Acropora* spp. *Periclimenaeus*, which lives in sponges, and *Thalassina*, which burrows in mud.

Desirable/undesirable features: Ornamental. Useful in reef aquariums. Harmful to small fishes. Reef safe.

Food: Carnivorous, scavenger.

Special considerations: Provide sand or gravel substrate for them to build their burrows.

Hardiness in captivity: Hardy. Life span- years.

Axiopsis, *Callianassa* and *Thalassina*

Common Name: Ghost Shrimp, Shrimp Lobster, Scorpion Mud Lobster

Region: Circumtropical and in temperate seas.

Description: Appearance between mantis shrimps and pistol shrimps. One claw larger than the other. The second set of legs has a dense fringe of fine hairs. Active burrowers that build extensive tunnel dwellings in rubble, sandbeds and in mud. Useful for aerating deep sandbeds in large aquariums.

Similar: Pistol shrimps and mantis shrimps.

Desirable/undesirable features: Useful in large reef aquariums. Reef safe.

Food: Omnivorous. Feeds on organic debris, detritus, bacteria, decomposing plants. Will take meaty foods, including worms.

Special considerations: Requires deep substrate or a specially constructed display composed of molded tunnels. Their burrowing can cause rock collapse.

Hardiness in captivity: Hardy. Life span - years.

Alpheus sp. from Florida.

Alpheus sp. from the Western Pacific.

Axiopsis cf. *serratifrons*.

Callianassa sp. in a unique display at the Monterey Bay Aquarium.

173

Odontodactylus

Common Name: Mantis Shrimp, Thumb splitter.

Region: Caribbean, Pacific, Arabian Sea, Indian Ocean

Description: *Odontodactylus scyallarus* has a green body, blue eyestalks, and red thoracic limbs. A very intelligent builder of burrows in coral rubble on reef slopes, it hunts at night for fish, mollusks, worms, and other crustaceans.

Similar: *Gonodactylus* spp.

Desirable/undesirable features: Ornamental. Destructive to tridacnid clams and worms. Harmful to people, invertebrates, and fishes. Not reef safe.

Food: Carnivorous.

Special considerations: Maintain in a display aquarium designed to feature them. Include coral rubble, gravel, and at least one rock. Not safe with fishes or most invertebrates, but can be kept with corals and anemones. Has powerful, sharp claws capable of piercing and splitting a finger.

Hardiness in captivity: Hardy. Life span - years.

Lysiosquillina and *Lysiosquilloides*

Common Name: Radar Mantis Shrimp

Region: Western Pacific

Description: These mantis shrimps have very distinctively shaped eyes that give the common name. They live in burrows in sandy areas, and may be brightly or cryptically colored.

Similar: *Lysiosquilla* and *Gonodactylus* spp.

Desirable/undesirable features: Ornamental. Destructive to tridacnid clams. Destructive to worms. Harmful to people. Harmful to invertebrates. Harmful to fishes. Not reef safe.

Food: Carnivorous.

Special considerations: Best maintained in a display aquarium designed to feature them. Include a thick gravel bed for burrowing.

Hardiness in captivity: Hardy. Life span - years.

Odontodactylus scyallarus is a colorful mantis shrimp from the Western Pacific. Atlantis, L.I. N.Y.

BAM! Mantis shrimp versus crab. Atlantis, Long Island, New York.

Lysiosquillina sp. Solomon Islands.

Lysiosquilloides sp. Solomon Islands.

175

Enoplometopus

Common Name: Reef Lobster

Region: Circumtropical

Description: Similar in appearance to freshwater crayfish. Secretive, living in burrows, caves, or crevices.

Similar: *Metanephrops* spp.

Desirable/undesirable features: Ornamental. Harmful to fishes. Reef safe.

Food: Carnivorous. Feeds on all meaty foods.

Special considerations: Include a thick gravel bed for burrowing, and rocks for hiding places. Keep solitary because they are territorial and very aggressive toward each other. Usually docile, but capable of harming small fishes. Addition of iodine rich foods or iodine supplement needed for proper molting.

Hardiness in captivity: Hardy. Life span - years.

Enoplometopus sp.

Enoplometopus sp.

Enoplometopus debelius is a spectacular pet!

177

Panulirus

Common Name: Spiny lobster

Region: Circumtropical

Description: *Panulirus versicolor* is the member of this genus most frequently seen in the aquarium trade. It has a distinctive blue tail.

Similar: *Justia*

Desirable/undesirable features: Ornamental. Harmful to small fishes and some invertebrates. Not reef safe.

Food: Carnivorous. Feeds on all meaty foods, especially clam meat.

Special considerations: Include a thick gravel bed for burrowing, and large rocks for hiding places. Usually docile, but capable of harming small fishes. Addition of iodine rich foods or iodine supplement needed for proper molting. They grow very large and can be destructive because of their excavating activities.

Hardiness in captivity: Hardy. Life span - years.

Panulirus versicolor from the Red Sea to central Pacific has white antennae and a blue tail.

Panulirus guttatus from Florida and the Caribbean is a small lobster with a vivid color pattern.

Justitia

Common Name: Long Arm Spiny Lobster

Region: Caribbean, West Atlantic, Pacific, Indian Ocean

Description: Similar to *Panulirus* spp. but has long false claws with curved tips. Color is usually orange with white spots and bands.

Similar: *Panulirus* spp.

Desirable/undesirable features: Ornamental. Harmful to small fishes and some invertebrates. Not reef safe.

Food: Carnivorous. Feeds on all meaty foods, especially clam meat.

Special considerations: Include a thick gravel bed for burrowing, and large rocks for hiding places. Usually docile, but capable of harming small fishes. Addition of iodine rich foods or iodine supplement needed for proper molting.

Hardiness in captivity: Hardy. Life span - years.

Justitia longimanus. Max Gibbs.

178

Palinurellus

Common Name: Copper Lobster, Furry Lobster

Region: Caribbean, West Atlantic, Pacific, Indian Ocean, Red Sea.

Description: Flattened carapace covered with short "fur", length to about 20 cm, orange color. Very secretive, spending most of the time hidden in the rocks or in caves. May burrow in sand. Active at night.

Similar: *Panulirus* spp.

Desirable/undesirable features: Ornamental. May be harmful to fishes. Reef safe.

Food: Carnivorous. Feeds on all meaty foods.

Special considerations: Usually docile, but capable of harming small fishes. Addition of iodine rich foods or iodine supplement needed for proper molting. Provide caves.

Hardiness in captivity: Hardy. Life span - years.

The copper lobster is a seldom seen reef inhabitant. Paul Humann.

Scyllarides

Common Name: Slipper, Spanish, or Shovel-Nosed Lobster.

Region: Circumtropical

Description: Flattened carapace with shovel shaped antennae used for digging.

Similar: *Parribacus* , which occurs circumtropically, *Arctides*, from the Pacific, Indian, Caribbean and Atlantic, *Scyllarus* from the Pacific, East Atlantic and Meditteranean, *Ibacus* from the West Pacific and *Thenus*, from the Red Sea, Indian, and Pacific.

Desirable/undesirable features: Ornamental. Harmful to small fishes and many types of invertebrates. Not reef safe.

Food: Carnivorous. Meaty foods, including clams, snails, worms, and other invertebrates.

Special considerations: Include a thick substrate for burrowing, and rocks. Capable of harming small fishes. Will eat clams, worms, other invertebrates. Addition of iodine rich foods or iodine supplement needed for proper molting.

Hardiness in captivity: Hardy. Life span - years.

Scyllarides aequinoctialis has a body specially suited for di

179

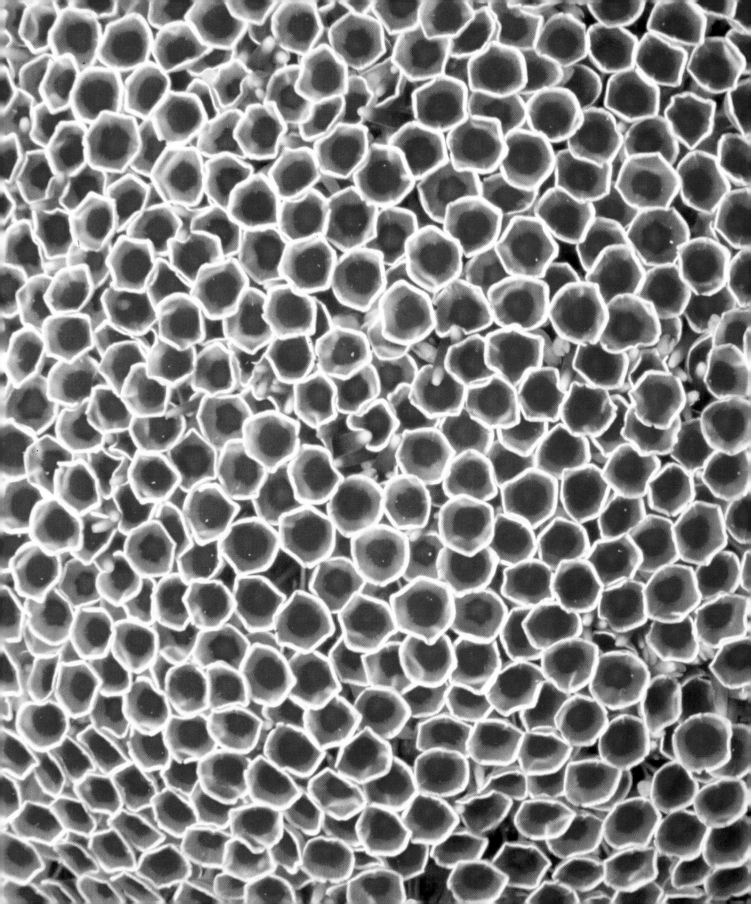

Echinoderms

Echinoderms (phylum Echinodermata) include familiar creatures such as sea stars a.k.a. "starfish," sand dollars, and sea urchins, as well as sea cucumbers, serpent stars, basket stars, crinoids, sea biscuits, and heart urchins. There are no freshwater echinoderms.

Echinoderms are frequently but not always "spiny skinned" creatures. Nevertheless, they all have an internal skeleton made of calcium carbonate. The skeleton may consist of tiny pieces called ossicles that fit together like articulating joints or beads, or it may be a box-like test composed of several plates sutured together. In some sea cucumbers the skeletal elements are tiny sand-like sclerites. In sea urchins the internal skeleton (test) has tubercles that form joints about which the calcium carbonate spines rotate.

Echinoderms all have a water vascular system that serves several functions. This water conducting system is believed to have evolved first as an apparatus for collecting and transporting food, later becoming an important means of achieving locomotion in certain mobile species. It also plays a role in gas exchange. The tube feet present in most seastars, sea urchins, and sea cucumbers extend and contract by the coordinated function of water conduction in the water vascular system. Likewise the extension, inflation and deflation of filter-feeding appendages in certain sea cucumbers is achieved by regulating water pressure to them. It is fascinating to watch this in large colorful species such as the Sea Apples, *Pseudocolochirus* spp. that inflate and deflate their feeding arms as they stuff them into and take them out of the mouth.

Although echinoderms lack a brain, their complex movements are mediated by sensory and nervous systems that achieve some remarkable feats. For example, serpent stars' sense of smell leads them to food at a rate of speed that suggests vision rather than smell. Although it is not reported in the scientific literature, anecdotal observations by aquarists seem to suggest that some echinoderms (sea stars and serpent stars) may possess the ability to become "trained" to expect food at a certain place and time. That ability suggests they have a form of memory.

It is no wonder that echinoderms are popular with aquarists. They are interesting to watch, beautiful, and often hardy in captivity. Some are not hardy, however, and some, though easy to keep, are toxic to fishes or humans.

Diadema

Common Name: Long-Spine Sea Urchin.

Region: Circumtropical.

Description: Black extremely elongate spines. Sometimes
with white or banded black and white spines. Body may have
red or blue pigment. The spines are extremely sharp, brittle,
and easily puncture skin where they break off, leaving a
painful wound. Excellent herbivores in reef aquaria but may
sometimes graze on corals. *Diadema setosum* has a distinctive
eye-like orange "iris" and black "pupil" on its anal sack.
Numerous fishes seek shelter between their spines.

Similar: *Arbacia* from north Florida and the Gulf of Mexico
has elongate black spines. *Astropyga radiata* is most similar,
but colored quite differently. *Echinothrix* spp. are very similar,
but clearly have two sets of spines, one thick and long, the
other thin and shorter. *Centrostephanus coronatus*, which
looks like a *Diadema*, is quite distinct in being nocturnal and a
carnivore! The other genera noted here are herbivores and
active during the day.

Desirable/undesirable features: Ornamental. Useful in reef
aquariums. Destructive or harmful to corals. Toxic or harmful
to people. Reef safe.

Food: Herbivorous. Carnivorous (when it eats corals).

Special considerations: Provide sufficient algae to graze or
feed dried seaweed (Nori). *Diadema* spp. have a strong
attraction to eat (completely)*Acropora palmata*, and may
lightly graze other corals, but usually do not harm them.

Hardiness in captivity: Hardy. *Diadema* spp. have been
spawned and reared in aquaculture projects. Life span - years.

Diadema setosum occurs from the Red Sea to the western Pacific. Oceanopolis, Brest, France.

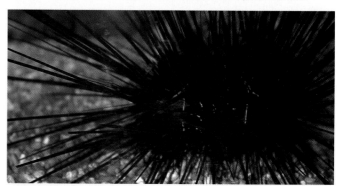

Diadema savignyi occurs from Africa to the Pacific. Oceanopolis, Brest, France.

Diadema setosum with an Arrow Blenny. Shrimpfishes and Cardinal fishes also associate with them.

Astropyga and *Echinothrix*

Common Name: Long-Spine Sea Urchin.

Region: Indian Ocean to the central Pacific, Caribbean.

Description: *Astropyga radiata* has brownish long sharp venomous spines and bright blue spots on the test. A translucent anal sack is located on top. Echinothrix spp. have two sets of spines, thick and thin. In *E. calamaris* the thicker spines are hollow and open at the tips.

Similar: *Diadema* spp.

Desirable/undesirable features: Ornamental. Useful in reef aquariums. Destructive or harmful to corals. Toxic or harmful to people. Reef safe.

Food: Herbivorous. Carnivorous.

Special considerations: Provide sufficient algae to graze or supplement with dried seaweed (Nori). Use care when handling!

Hardiness in captivity: Hardy. Life span - years.

Echinothrix calamaris has blue pigment in between the spines, and the thicker spines have open tips.

Astropyga radiata on a shallow seagrass bed in the Solomon Islands.

Asthenosoma

Common Name: Fire Urchin, Galloping Urchin.

Region: Red Sea to Western Pacific.

Description: Short, purple swollen venom-tipped spines and a flexible test. Spines held together in a pattern of clusters until the urchin is disturbed. *Asthenosoma varium* is a host to commensal shrimps, snails, and juvenile fishes that gain protection from predators between its toxic spines. It is called Galloping Urchin because of its rapid army-tank-like movements.

Similar: *Asthenosoma ijimai* is similar to *Salmacis bicolor*.

Desirable/undesirable features: Ornamental. Destructive or harmful to corals. Toxic or harmful to people. Reef safe.

Food: Herbivorous. Carnivorous.

Special considerations: Provide sufficient algae to graze or supplement with dried seaweed (Nori). Use care when handling! The sting is excruciating, like an electric shock.

Hardiness in captivity: Hardy. Life span - years.

Asthenosoma varium.

Asthenosoma varium. Country Critters, Long Island, New York.

Toxopneustes

Common Name: Flower Urchin

Region: Indian Ocean to the Eastern Pacific

Description: Short inconspicuous spines hidden by large, flower-like pedicillaria. The pedicillaria have venomous teeth that quickly adhere upon being touched and inject their poison. *Toxopneustes pileolus* is considered extremely venomous and is reported to have caused fatalities in humans.

Similar: None.

Desirable/undesirable features: Ornamental. Destructive or harmful to corals. Toxic or harmful to people. Reef safe.

Food: Herbivorous.

Special considerations: Provide algae to graze. Supplement with dried seaweed. Use care when handling! Keep out of reach of children! Should not be harvested for home aquaria, or the distribution chain should maintain a warning label with the animal at all times to warn all who come in contact with it.

Hardiness in captivity: Hardy. Life span - years.

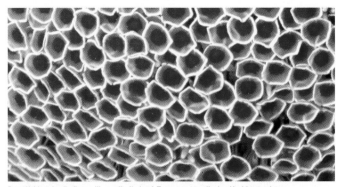

Beautiful but deadly flower-like pedicellaria of *Toxopneustes pileolus.* Kushimoto, Japan.

Toxopneustes sp. Aquarium photo, Rome, Italy.

184

Lytechinus

Common Name: Pin-Cushin Urchin, Short-Spined Urchin, Variegated Urchin, Jewel Urchin.

Region: Caribbean, Eastern Pacific.

Description: Short sharp spines and clear colorless or slightly pigmented pedicillaria. Often covered by shells, sponges, or algae held by the pedicillaria for camouflage and shade. The color of the spines is variable, including white, green, pink, and purple. Common on seagrass, reefs, and rocky shorelines.

Similar: *Pseudoboletia, Tripneustes*, and *Salmacis* spp.

Desirable/undesirable features: Ornamental. Useful in reef aquariums. Destructive or harmful to corals. Reef safe.

Food: Herbivorous.

Special considerations: Provide sufficient algae to graze or supplement with dried seaweed. Large specimens may knock over corals and thus are not desirable in reef aquariums.

Hardiness in captivity: Hardy. Life span - years.

Lytechinus variegatus in its natural habitat on a seagrass bed. Key Biscayne, Florida.

Salmacis sp. Exotic Aquariums, Miami Florida.

Pseudoboletia maculata is very similar to *Lytechinus variegatus*.

Tripneustes

Common Name: Sea Egg.

Region: Caribbean, Red Sea, to Central Pacific.

Description: Short sharp white spines with areas of pigmented pedicillaria. Often covered by shells, sponges, or algae picked up by the urchin and held by the pedicillaria for camouflage and shade.

Similar: *Asthenosoma, Lytechinus* and *Pseudoboletia* spp.

Desirable/undesirable features: Ornamental. Useful in reef aquariums. Destructive or harmful to corals. Reef safe.

Food: Herbivorous.

Special considerations: Provide sufficient algae to graze or supplement with dried seaweed (Nori). Large specimens may knock over corals and thus are not desirable in reef aquariums.

Hardiness in captivity: Hardy. Life span - years.

Tripneustes ventricosus, Key Biscayne, Florida.

Tripneustes gratilla in its natural habitat on a seagrass bed, Solomon Islands.

A particularly colorful *Tripneustes gratilla* accompanied by a yellow brotulid, aquarium photo.

Mespilla

Common Name: Globe Urchin.

Region: Western and Central Pacific.

Description: Ten bright blue or green naked regions between rows of short sharp spines. *Mespilla globulus* is a hardy species that is popular in reef aquariums for the control of filamentous algae.

Similar: *Microcyphus* from the Red Sea and Indian Ocean has an undulating edge to the naked regions (which are pinkish) between spines, but is otherwise similar.

Desirable/undesirable features: Ornamental. Useful in reef aquariums. Destructive or harmful to some corals. Reef safe.

Food: Herbivorous.

Special considerations: Provide sufficient algae to graze or supplement with dried seaweed (Nori). May occasionally graze on soft corals, particularly nephtheidae.

Hardiness in captivity: Hardy. Life span - years.

Mespilla globulus is an excellent and attractive small herbivore for reef aquariums.

Colobocentrotus

Common Name: Rock Urchin.

Region: East Africa to Hawaii.

Description: Purplish black urchin with a row of paddle-shaped spines on the periphery tightly held against the rock, and scale-like spines on the dome-shaped aboral surface. It inhabits intertidal shore rocks exposed to heavy surf. Its shape prevents it from being torn from the rocks by the waves.

Similar: None.

Desirable/undesirable features: Ornamental. Reef safe*.

Food: Herbivorous.

Special considerations: *Not suitable for typical home aquariums or reef aquariums because of the requirement for wave action. Maintained at the Waikiki Aquarium with special surge device. Sensitive to low oxygen levels. Provide sufficient algae to graze or supplement with dried seaweed (Nori).

Hardiness in captivity: Poor in typical aquariums, hardy in specially designed surge tanks. Life span - years.

Colobocentrotus atratus does not survive in typical aquariums. Bruce Carlson.

Echinometra

Common Name: Rock Urchin, Rock Boring Urchin

Region: Circumtropical

Description: Intertidal and subtidal on rocky coasts. Bores rounded holes in limesone rock. Color varies from black to brown, green, or red, some with a white ring at the base of each spine. Gobies and shrimps seek refuge beneath their spines in the excavated limestone holes.

Similar: *Parasalenia* spp. are more oval shaped with asymmetrically arranged skeletal plates. *Arbacia punctulata* and *Diadema* spp. have longer spines.

Desirable/undesirable features: Ornamental. Destructive or harmful to corals. Not reef safe.

Food: Herbivorous.

Special considerations: Provide live algae or supplement with dried seaweed (Nori). They erode rocks, causing structural problems in reef aquariums. Safe in fish aquariums.

Hardiness in captivity: Hardy. Life span - years.

Echinometra sp. Miami Beach, FL.

Echinometra sp. Miami Beach, FL.

A beautiful *Echinometra* sp. from *Indonesia*.

Arbacia punctulata, Reef and Fin, Connecticut.

Heterocentrotus

Common Name: Slate Pencil Urchin.

Region: Red Sea to central Pacific.

Description: Large smooth club-shaped spines that taper at the tips. Often bright reddish salmon colored, with or without white stripes on the spines. Hardy herbivore but capable of knocking over or breaking rocks. Not ideal for small reef aquariums.

Similar: *Eucidaris, Phyllacanthus*, and *Prionocidaris*

Desirable/undesirable features: Ornamental. Destructive or harmful to corals. Not reef safe.

Food: Herbivorous.

Special considerations: Provide sufficient algae to graze or supplement with dried seaweed (Nori). These active grazers strongly erode rocks and corals, and bulldoze the reef structure such that their presence in a reef aquarium is sure to cause structural problems. They are safe in a fish aquarium.

Hardiness in captivity: Hardy. Life span - years.

Heterocentrotus mammillatus. Aquarium photo, Reef International, Milan.

Heterocentrotus mammillatus. Aquarium photo, Reef International, Milan.

Eucidaris

Common Name: Pencil Urchin

Region: Circumtropical

Description: Members of this group, known as cidaroid urchins, have a sparse number of thick, blunt spines supported by rings of small plates (basal spines). In *Eucidaris* spp. the spines have rows of low tubercles on them. *Eucidaris* spp. are omnivores, feeding on algae, seagrass, sponges, bryozoans, clams, snails. They have even been reported to trap (with their spines) and eat fishes.

Similar: *Prionocidaris* and *Phyllacanthus* from the Red Sea and Indo-Pacific regions have the same basic cidaroid architecture but quite distinctly different spine ornamentation. *Heterocentrotus* spp., known as Slate Pencil Urchins, have smooth club-shaped spines.

Desirable/undesirable features: Ornamental. Destructive or harmful to corals. May harm small fishes. Not reef safe.

Food: Herbivorous.

Special considerations: Provide sufficient algae to graze or supplement with dried seaweed (Nori). Destructive in reef aquariums, disturbing the stability of the rock decoration. Safe in a fish aquarium.

Hardiness in captivity: Hardy. Life span - years.

The Pencil Urchin, *Eucidaris tribuloides* from the Caribbean.

Phyllacanthus imperialis, closeup. Solomon Islands.

Clypeaster, Lovenia and **Maretia**

Common Name: Heart Urchin, Sea Biscuit.

Region: Caribbean, Indo-Pacific

Description: Sand dwelling burrowing urchins with short or bristly brush-like spines. Relatives of sand dollars, these active urchins are consumers of detritus and possibly specific creatures living in the sand. Very effective at cleaning deep sand beds, but short-lived in small aquariums.

Similar: other heart urchins, including *Brissus* and *Echinoneus*.

Desirable/undesirable features: Useful in reef aquariums. Reef safe.

Food: Omnivorous, detritivore.

Special considerations: Aquarium size Diet.

Hardiness in captivity: Not hardy. Life span -months.

Maretia cf. *planulata* may be found above the sand at night. Max Gibbs.

Maretia cf. *planulata* digging into the sand. Max Gibbs.

191

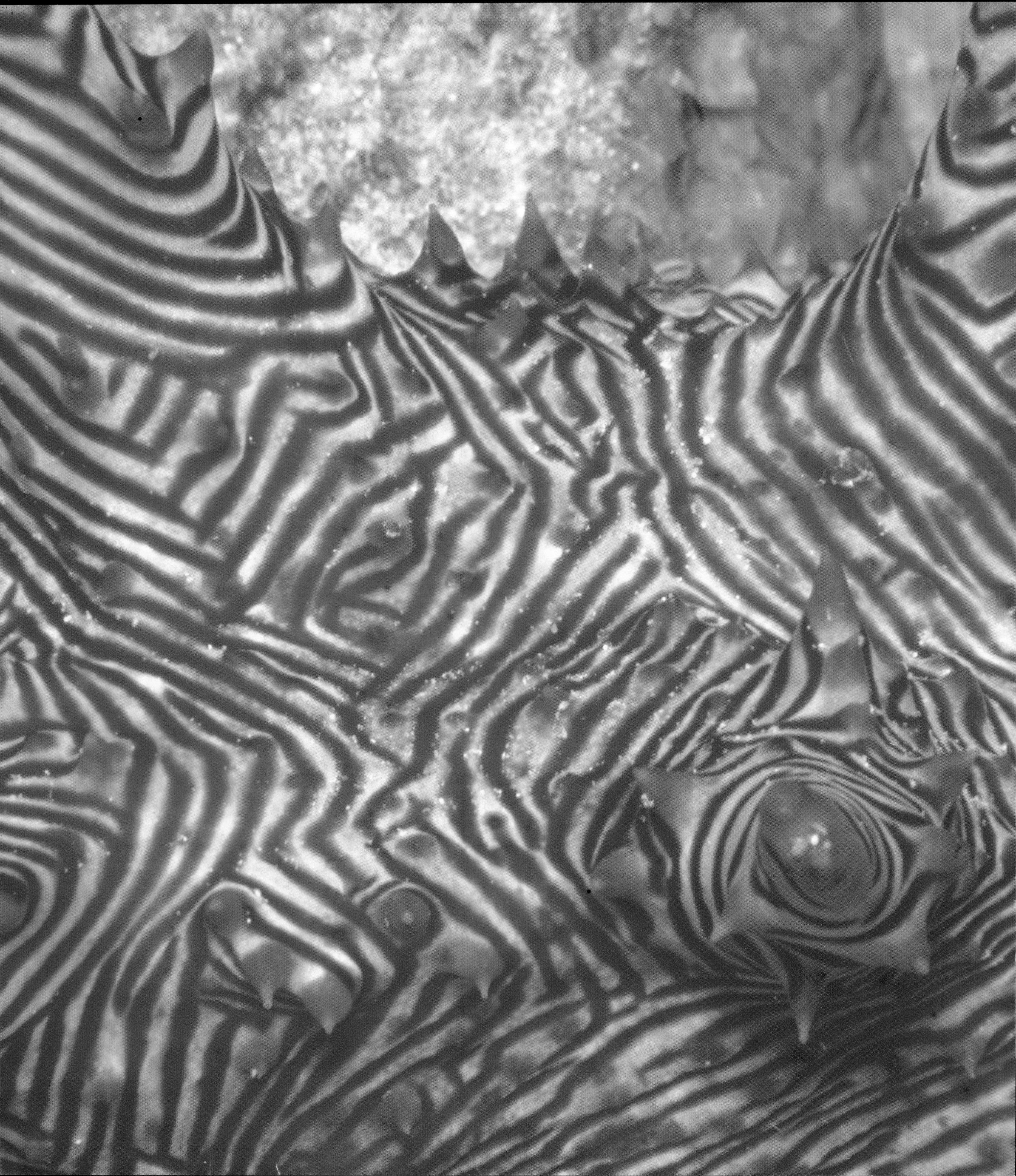

Holothuria

Common Name: Tigertail, Donkey Dung, "trepang," "beche de mer."

Region: Circumtropical and in temperate seas.

Description: *Holothuria (Halodeima) atra* from the Red Sea to Hawaii is completely black. *Holothuria (Halodeima) edulis* has a dark dorsal surface and pinkish or reddish ventral surface. *Holothuria (Halodeima) floridana* is a common, variably colored species collected in Florida for aquariums. There are probably several genera classified in this genus, but all mop up sand and detritus to obtain their food. Excellent for reef aquariums with sandy bottoms. *Holothuria (Thymiosycia) thomasi*, the Tigertail seacucumber from the Caribbean, reaches a length in excess of 6 feet. It remains hidden in coral or coral rock during the day, and extends its oral end to mop up the surrounding sand at night.

Similar: There are so many varieties under this genus no encompassing comparison can be made.

Desirable/undesirable features: Useful in reef aquariums. Toxic or harmful to fishes. Reef safe.

Food: Detritivore.

Special considerations: Harmed by pump intakes or overflow drains. Injured animals may release mild or potent toxins, harmful to fish.
Aquarium size: Do not put too many in an aquarium as they quickly consume all available food in the substrate. As a general rule of thumb- stock aquariums with about 3 inches of seacucumber per 20 gallons. The tigertail is an exception to this rule.

Hardiness in captivity: Hardy. Some species may reproduce vegetatively, by fission. Life span - years.

Holothuria (Halodeima) edulis. Red Sea to Pacific. Country Critters, Long Island, New York.

Holothuria (Halodeima) atra from the Red Sea to the Pacific.

Holothuria (Halodeima) floridana. Common color pattern. Florida Keys.

Holothuria (Thymiosycia) hilla from the Red Sea to Pacific. Country Critters, Long Island, New York.

Holothuria (Halodeima) floridana. Yellow morph. Florida Keys.

193

Pseudocolochirus

Common Name: Sea Apple.

Region: A narrow range in the Indo-Pacific (Australia, Phillipines, Indonesia, Sri Lanka, India, Vietnam, China, Hong Kong, Japan).

Description: Colorful rounded sea cucumbers that extend highly branched feeding tentacles to trap planktonic food. Three distinct color forms exist, and four species names exist in the literature: *P. violaceus, P. axiologus, P. tricolor,* and *P. arae.* There may be three species, two, or just one with regional color differences. The "Australian Sea Apple" *P. axiologus* is primarily blue, with red tube feet and a white-tipped violet and red crown of feeding tentacles. The Philippine variety, *P. violaceus,* is more variable in color, sometimes being mostly red, blue, half and half, or purple, but always with yellow tube feet. Its crown of tentacles is usually red with yellow tips, but sometimes blue or purple and the oral region is nearly always blue-violet. The third variety, the Royal Sea Apple, is rare and very distinctive. It is stunningly dark blue-violet, with yellow tube feet, sometimes with a white border separating the yellow of the tube feet from the violet color of the body. The crown of oral tentacles is magenta or violet.

Similar: Pentacta, which has distinctive large knoby projections. *Neothyonidium magnum* (family Phyllophoridae) that live buried in the sand and extend highly branched arms to trap planktonic food.

Desirable/undesirable features: Ornamental. Toxic or harmful to fishes. Reef safe.

Food: Detritivore. Feeds on particulate and dissolved organic matter, "marine snow," phytoplankton, algal fragments, and zooplankton.

Special considerations: Should not be housed with fishes. The eggs are toxic. Harmed by pump intakes or overflow drains. Injured animals may release potent toxins. Must be fed daily (liquid foods or spray-dried algae for filter-feeding invertebrates) or it will slowly starve, evidenced by shrinking body and degeneration of feeding tentacles. Provide strong current to stimulate feeding.

Hardiness in captivity: Hardy. Life span - years.

The Royal Sea Apple, *Pseudocolochirus* sp. is rare, beautiful, and very expensive. Max Gibbs.

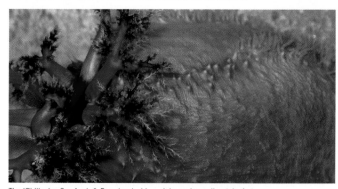

The "Australian Sea Apple," *Pseudocolochirus axiologus* has red tube feet.

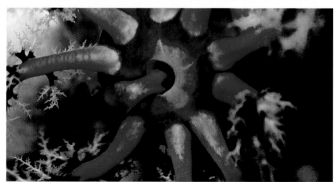

The "Philippine Sea Apple," *Pseudocolochirus violaceus* has yellow tube feet.

It is fascinating to watch *Pseudocolochirus violaceus* stuff its branched tentacles into its mouth.

Colochirus

Common Name: Yellow cucumber.

Region: Indo-Pacific.

Description: Sea slug-like small (to about 1.5 inches) yellow filter-feeding sea cucumbers that adhere to the substrate in areas with strong currents. Extend food gathering arms.

Similar: *Pentacta anceps*, which is larger and pink. Caribbean and Eastern Pacific reefs have similar gray or black filter feeding sea cucumbers..

Desirable/undesirable features: Ornamental. Toxic or harmful to fishes. Reef safe.

Food: Detritivore. Feeds on particulate and dissolved organic matter, "marine snow," phytoplankton, and tiny zooplankton.

Special considerations: Harmed by pump intakes or overflow drains. Injured animals may release mild toxins. Feed daily or it will slowly starve, evidenced by shrinking body and degeneration of feeding tentacles. Currents stimulate feeding.

Hardiness in captivity: Hardy. Life span - years.

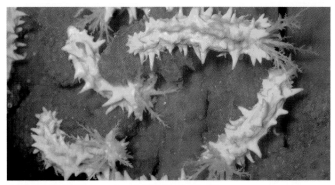

Colochirus robustus often occurs in small aggregations in the wild.

Colochirus robustus is hardy in reef aquariums when fed sufficient particulate organic food.

Pentacta

Common Name: Spiny Sea Cucumber

Region: Indo-Pacific

Description: *Pentacta anceps* is pinkish, with yellow and pink feeding tentacles, and grows to eight inches in length.

Similar: *Colochirus*. Spiny specimens may be a *Colochirus* sp. *Pentacta anceps* looks the same but lacks spines.

Desirable/undesirable features: Ornamental. Toxic or harmful to fishes. Reef safe.

Food: Detritivore. Feeds on particulate and dissolved organic matter, "marine snow," phytoplankton, and zooplankton.

Special considerations: Harmed by pump intakes or overflow drains. Injured animals may release mild or potent toxins. Must be fed daily (liquid or spray-dried foods for filter-feeding invertebrates) or it will slowly starve, evidenced by shrinking body and degeneration of feeding tentacles. Provide strong current to stimulate feeding.

Hardiness in captivity: Hardy. Life span - years.

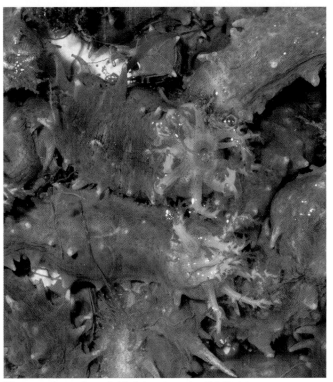

This sea cucumber sometimes called *Pentacta anceps* may be a *Colochirus* sp.

Synapta, *Euapta*, and *Synaptula*

Common Name: Medusa Worm.

Region: Circumtropical.

Description: Members of the order Apodida have transparent tissue and very soft and flexible bodies that lack tube feet but contain numerous tiny sclerites that make the skin extremely sticky. The feeding tentacles have pinnules that make them look like feathers, much like the tentacles of soft corals. Very active feeders on detritus, some are associated with sponges, where they clean trapped microalgae and detritus from the sponge surface and feed on sponge exudates.

Similar: *Opheodesoma* spp.

Desirable/undesirable features: Ornamental. Toxic or harmful to fishes. Reef safe.

Food: Detritivore. Feeds on particulate and dissolved organic matter, "marine snow," phytoplankton, and zooplankton.

Special considerations: Harmed by pump intakes or overflow drains. Large specimens of free living *Synapta*, *Euapta*, and *Opheodesoma* are fantastic to observe in aquariums, but should not be housed with fishes because they release potent toxic compounds in the water when injured, resulting in fish kills. Some small species that proliferate vegetatively and live among seaweeds are safe to house with fishes.

Hardiness in captivity: Hardy. Life span - years.

Medusa worm, *Euapta godeffroyi*, Solomon Islands.

Synaptula spp. occur in large aggregations on sponges.

Another "Medusa Worm," *Synapta maculata*, closeup of feeding tentacles.

Synapta maculata.

A section of the elongate body of a *Euapta godeffroyi*, Solomon Islands.

197

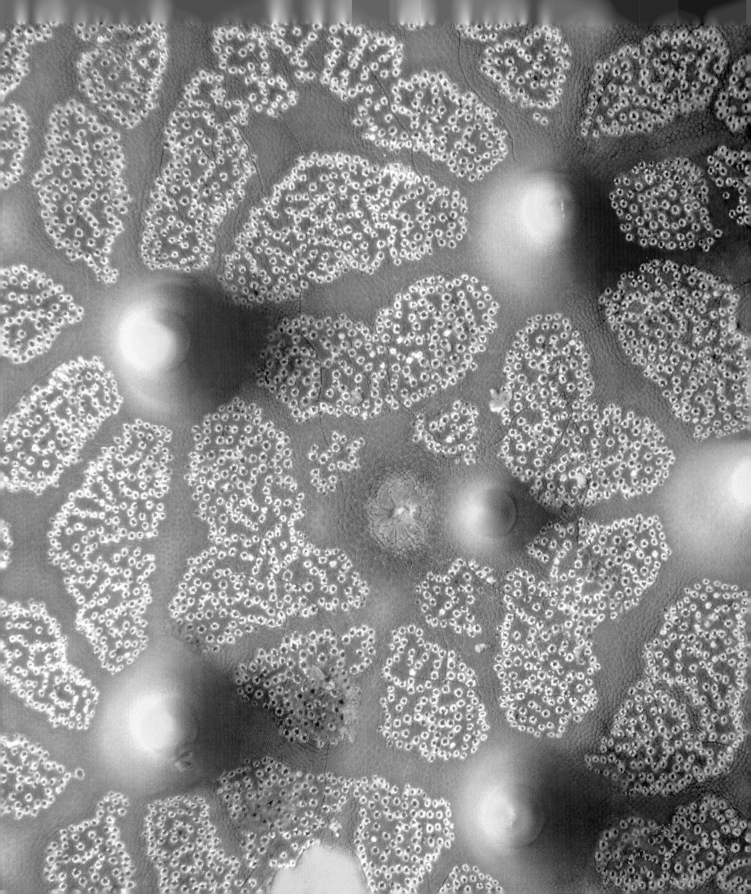

Pentaceraster

Common Name: Cushion Star.

Region: Red Sea, Indo-Pacific, Hawaii to Eastern Pacific.

Description: Several species, all with hard dorsal conical spines. Found on seagrass beds, sandy areas and reef flats.

Similar: *Oreaster reticulatus* from the Caribbean, *Pentaster* and *Protoreaster* from the Indo-Pacific region.

Desirable/undesirable features: Ornamental. May be destructive to tridacnid clams or harmful to invertebrates. Not reef safe.

Food: Herbivorous. Herbivorous. Carnivorous. Detritivore. Feeds on sponges and microorganisms, as well as scavenges dead mollusks, urchins, and algae. Feed clams, squid meat.

Special considerations: It will graze on algae and microfauna on live rock and sand, so it is beneficial to its health to maintain it with live rock and a sand or gravel substrate. Should be fed additionally at least once per week.

Hardiness in captivity: Hardy. Life span - years.

Protoreaster (foreground) and *Pentaceraster* are hardy aquarium inhabitants but voracious predators.

Pentaceraster alveolatus in its natural habitat on a seagrass bed. Solomon Islands.

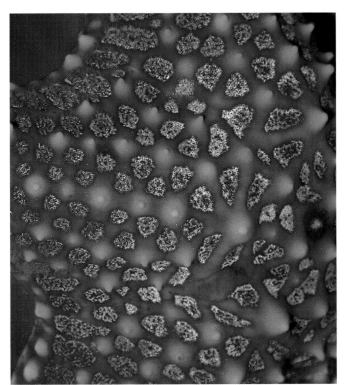

Pentaceraster cf. *cumingi* from the Eastern Pacific.

Oreaster reticulatus, the common Bahama Star from Florida and the Caribbean.

Protoreaster

Common Name: Chocolate Chip Star, African Sea Star.

Region: West Africa to the central Pacific.

Description: *Protoreaster nodosus* is the common Chocolate Chip Star found on sand and seagrass beds in the Indian Ocean to central Pacific. *Protoreaster lincki* is a stunningly colored sea star in gray and bright red.

Similar: *Pentaceraster.*

Desirable/undesirable features: Ornamental. May be destructive to tridacnid clams or harmful to invertebrates. Not reef safe.

Food: Herbivorous. Carnivorous. Detritivore. Sponges and microorganisms, and live or dead mollusks, urchins, anemones, and algae. Feed chopped clam meat, squid.

Special considerations: Maintain in an aquarium with a sand or gravel. Feed once per week. Not suitable for reef aquariums because they eat anemones, sponges, and clams.

Hardiness in captivity: Hardy. Life span - years.

Protoreaster nodosus in its natural habitat on a seagrass bed. Solomon Islands.

Protoreaster nodosus, the "Chocolate Chip Seastar" is hardy, but is not suitable for reef aquariums.

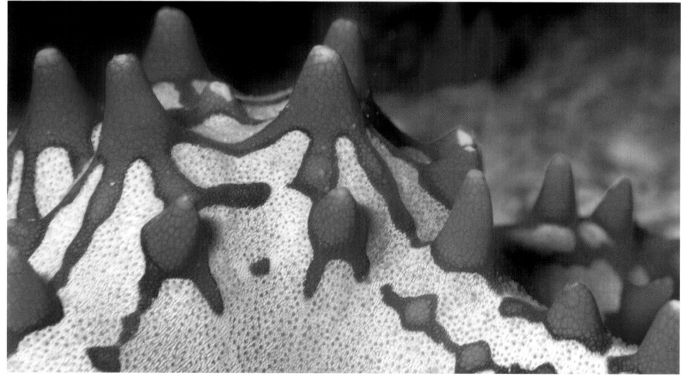

The spectacularly colored *Protoreaster lincki* feeds on sponges, bacterial films, and clams in its natural habitat on seagrass beds.

Asterina

Common Name: Asterina

Region: Circumtropical

Description: Very small sea star, some only 1/4 inch in diameter, others up to about 1 inch. Three species are commonly imported with live rock. A small whitish *Asterina* sp. feeds on algae on the aquarium glass. Other larger species may sometimes feed on coral tissue and are dangerous in a reef aquarium because they proliferate rapidly by fission.

Similar: none

Desirable/undesirable features: May be destructive or harmful to corals. Some species are reef safe. They may be utilized as food for *Hymenocera* sp. shrimp

Food: Herbivorous. Some eat coral tissue.

Special considerations: Monitor them to be sure they don't eat the corals.

Hardiness in captivity: Hardy. Reproduce prolifically. Life span - years.

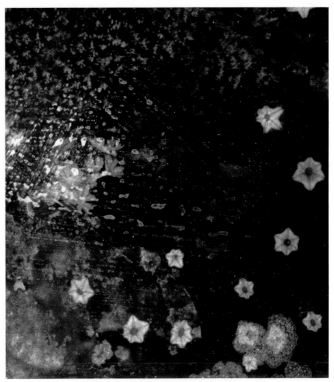

This small whitish *Asterina* sp. feeds on algal films on the aquarium glass.

Asterina sp. feeding on a stony coral.

A large *Asterina* sp. is only 1/2 inch across.

Acanthaster

Common Name: Crown of Thorns Starfish (Sea Star), COTS

Region: Indian Ocean to Eastern Pacific

Description: Sea star with 10 to 20 arms covered dorsally with long sharp spines that can cause serious and painful wounds. Eats the tissues of stony corals. In Thailand and localities in the Indian ocean specimens may be very colorful in shades of magenta and blue. Elsewhere they are normally grayish green, dull reddish, or brown.

Similar: *Heliaster kubiniji*, the Gulf Sun Star from Baja California, the Gulf of California to Nicaragua.

Desirable/undesirable features: Ornamental. Destructive or harmful to corals. Toxic to people. Not reef safe.

Food: Herbivorous. Carnivorous. Feeds on coral tissue & algae.

Special considerations: Use caution when handling, feed algae and coral tissue. Should not be imported for aquariums.

Hardiness in captivity: Hardy. Life span - years.

Acanthaster planci feeding on coral. Marj Awai.

The spines of *Acanthaster planci* are very sharp and can cause painful wounds. Marj Awai.

Acanthaster planci. Bruce Carlson.

202

Culcita

Common Name: Pin Cushion Star, Pillow Star, Biscuit Star.

Region: Red Sea to central Pacific.

Description: Fat seastar shaped like a pincushion or with very short arms. Color is variable.

Similar: Juveniles could be confused with *Asterina*.

Desirable/undesirable features: Ornamental. Destructive or harmful to corals. Not reef safe.

Food: Herbivorous. Carnivorous. Feeds on algae and coral tissue, mollusks, and bacterial films. Feed clam meat, Dried seaweed (Nori).

Special considerations: It will graze on algae and microfauna on live rock, so it is beneficial to its health to maintain it in an aquarium with live rock. Must be fed additionally at least once per week.

Hardiness in captivity: Hardy. Life span - years.

Biscuit star feeding on coral. Solomon Islands.

Closeup view of the underside of *Culcita novaeguineae*. Solomon Islands.

Fromia and *Neoferdina*

Common Name: Elegant Sea Star

Region: Red Sea to Central Pacific

Description: Many species (about 12) of small dorso-ventrally flattened sea stars with colorful patterns in shades of red, orange and yellow.

Similar: *Pentagonaster* and *Ferdina. Celerina heffernani* is very similar to and easily confused with *Fromia monilis.*

Desirable/undesirable features: Ornamental. Reef safe.

Food: Herbivorous. Carnivorous. Detritivore.

Special considerations: Though hardy when handled properly, they are sensitive to changes in specific gravity, temperature, pH and oxygen levels encountered during shipping, and may succumb to rapid bacterial infections that cause necrosis of the legs or whole body. Keep with live rock, from which they graze algae and microorganisms.

Hardiness in captivity: Delicate to acclimate.
Life span - years, with care.

Unidentified *Fromia* sp. Possibly *Ferdina* sp.

Neoferdina cf. *insolita.* Solomon Islands.

204

Fromia monilis is an attractive omnivorous seastar from Singapore, Kenny Tan.

Fromia nodosa is surprisingly cryptic in the natural environment. Singapore, Kenny Tan.

Fromia sp. Singapore, Kenny Tan.

Fromia indica is a hardy omnivorous seastar from Singapore, Kenny Tan.

Nardoa

Common Name: Galathea Sea Star.

Region: Western Pacific.

Description: Thick arms taper toward the tips, with bumps on the aboral surface. Spotted brown, yellow, and orange.

Similar: *Fromia indica, F. elegans,* and *Gomophia* spp.

Desirable/undesirable features: Ornamental. Reef safe. May be harmful to some invertebrates, such as clams or small anemones.

Food: Herbivorous. Carnivorous. Detritivore.

Special considerations: Though hardy when handled properly, they are sensitive to changes in specific gravity, temperature, pH and oxygen levels encountered during shipping, and may succumb to rapid bacterial infections that cause necrosis of the legs or whole body. Keep with live rock, from which they graze algae and microorganisms.

Hardiness in captivity: Hardy. Delicate to acclimate. Life span - years.

Nardoa novaecaledoniae. Sea Dwelling Creatures. Los Angeles, California.

Nardoa spp. are common and hardy seastars from the Western Pacific.

Phataria

Common Name: Tan Sea Star

Region: Eastern Pacific.

Description: Pale purplish gray, tan, or reddish brown with long tapering cylindrical arms and slender stiff body. Found on coralline algae coated rocks. Believed to be herbivorous.

Similar: Similar to *Linckia* and *Leiaster.*

Desirable/undesirable features: Ornamental. Reef safe. May harm some invertebrates, such as clams or sponges.

Food: Herbivorous. Carnivorous. Detritivore.

Special considerations: Sensitive to changes in specific gravity, temperature, pH and oxygen. May succumb to rapid bacterial infections that cause necrosis of the legs. Keep with live rock, from which they graze algae and microorganisms. Offer dried seaweed (Nori) or small bits of clam meat, placed under this sea star. Keep below 80 degrees Farenheight.

Hardiness in captivity: Hardy. Delicate to acclimate. Life span - years.

An especially colorful *Phataria* sp. Note the flattened margins of the arms and tapered tips.

Phataria sp. in an aquarium. House of Fins, Connecticut.

Tamaria and *Leiaster*

Common Name: Tamarisk Sea Star, Purple (Velvet) Sea Star.

Region: Eastern Pacific.

Description: Dark purple or magenta colored sea star. *Leiaster teres* has a shiny or velvety appearance, due to tiny finger-like respiratory papillae on its surface, and it grows to nearly 18 inches in diameter. Its arms are long and cylindrical, not strongly tapering to the tips. *Tamaria stria* is similarly colored, but much smaller, to only about 8 inches in diameter and with more strongly tapering arms.

Similar: *Linckia*.

Desirable/undesirable features: Ornamental. Reef safe. May be harmful to some invertebrates, such as clams, sponges, or small anemones.

Food: Herbivorous. Carnivorous. Detritivore.

Special considerations: Though hardy when handled properly, they are sensitive to changes in specific gravity, temperature, pH and oxygen levels encountered during shipping, and may succumb to rapid bacterial infections that cause necrosis of the legs or whole body. Keep with live rock, from which they graze algae and microorganisms. Offer dried seaweed (Nori) or small bits of clam meat, placed under this sea star.

Hardiness in captivity: Hardy. Delicate to acclimate. Life span - years.

Leiaster cf. *teres* has a stunning deep magenta hue.

Tamaria cf. *stria*.

207

Linckia

Common Name: Blue Star, Comet Star.

Region: Caribbean, Indo-Pacific.

Description: Several species are collected for aquariums. *Linckia laevigata*, the blue one from the Indo-Pacific region is the most common one. Arms smooth and cylindrical. Common on reef flats and rubble zones. Arms break easily and may regenerate whole seastars. The name "Comet" refers to a single arm with four new small arms, a product of such breakage and regeneration.

Similar: *Tamaria, Leiaster, Ophidiaster, Chaetaster.*

Desirable/undesirable features: Ornamental. Reef safe. May be harmful to some invertebrates, such as sponges.

Food: Omnivorous, feeding on bacterial films, sponges, and dead mollusks.

Special considerations: Though hardy when handled properly, they are sensitive to changes in specific gravity, temperature, pH and oxygen levels encountered during shipping, and may succumb to rapid bacterial infections that cause necrosis of the legs or whole body. A parasitic cap-shaped snail, *Thyca crystallina* commonly occurs on the oral side of the arms, and is usually colored to blend with its host. It tightly adheres there and inserts its feeding proboscis into ambulacral groove to suck out fluid and tissue from the sea star. Inspect *Linckia* spp. for this parasite and remove it if present. Keep with live rock and sand, from which they graze algae and microorganisms. Offer small bits of clam meat, placed under this sea star.

Hardiness in captivity: Hardy. Delicate to acclimate. Life span - years.

Linckia laevigata, the blue sea star on a reef in the Solomon Islands.

Linckia multiflora is easy to see when illuminated by the camera's strobe. Under natural light, however, it blends perfectly with live rock.

Linckia laevigata witth an orange *Echinaster luzonicus* riding on its back. Solomon Islands.

Linckia multiflora, right, with a *Fromia* sp. Solomon Islands.

Echinaster

Common Name: Spiny Seastar.

Region: Caribbean, Indian Ocean and Pacific.

Description: *Echinaster* (*Othilia*) *echinophorus* from the Caribbean is a blunt-armed, spiny orange seastar common in bays and seagrass beds, where it feeds on sponges. Its relative, *E.* (*Othilia*) *sentus* from Florida has longer arms that are less spiny, and it is common in bays where it feeds on sponges. *Echinaster callosus* is a spectacular beauty from the Indian Ocean and Western Pacific, where it occurs on coral reefs. It is slimy and rather limp, but can become rigid. The body has soft knobs and ridges that form rings on the rather elongate arms. *Echinaster luzonicus* has a smooth surface and tapering arms (usually five but often six), and may be bright red, orange, or brownish. It often carries the commensal ctenophore, *Ctenoplana astericola*, which is also featured in this book.

Similar: Three of the mentioned seastars are so distinctly different from each other that it's a wonder they are placed in the same genus. *Seriaster regularis* and *Nepanthia briareus* can be confused with *Echinaster luzonicus*.

Desirable/undesirable features: Ornamental. Reef safe. May harm clams, sponges, or small anemones.

Food: Herbivorous. Carnivorous. Detritivore.

Special considerations: Though hardy when handled properly, they are sensitive to changes in specific gravity, temperature, pH and oxygen levels encountered during shipping, and may succumb to rapid bacterial infections that cause necrosis of the legs or whole body. Keep with live rock, from which they graze algae and microorganisms. Offer dried seaweed (Nori) or small bits of clam meat, placed under this sea star.

Hardiness in captivity: Hardy. Some spp. reproduce in aquariums. Larvae develop in the gravel. Life span - years.

Echinaster luzonicus.

Echinaster (*Othilia*) *echinophorus* from the Caribbean. All Seas Fisheries, Miami Florida.

Echinaster callosus. Solomon Islands.

Mithrodia

Common Name: Spiny Sea Star, Studded Sea Star.

Region: Caribbean, Indo-Pacific.

Description: Arms with numerous prominent knobby protuberances. Most species are medium sized, up to about 8 inches in diameter. One species in the Western Pacific grows enormous. During a night dive the author saw a specimen at least 30 inches in diameter that walked extremely quickly across the reef.

Similar: *Nardoa frianti, Gomophia egyptiaca.*

Desirable/undesirable features: Ornamental. Reef safe. May be harmful to some invertebrates, such as sponges, clams or snails.

Food: Carnivorous. Herbivorous. Detritivore.

Special considerations: Though hardy when handled properly, they are sensitive to changes in specific gravity, temperature, pH and oxygen levels encountered during shipping, and may succumb to rapid bacterial infections that cause necrosis of the legs or whole body. Keep with live rock, from which they graze algae and microorganisms. Offer dried seaweed (Nori) or small bits of clam meat, placed under this sea star.

Hardiness in captivity: Hardy. Delicate to acclimate. Life span - years.

Mithrodia spp. seastars have characteristic knobs on the arms. They are voracious predators.

This enormous *Mithrodia* sp. seen at night was at least 30 inches (76 cm) across!

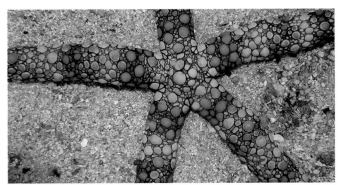

Nardoa frianti could be confused with *Mithrodia* and *Gomophia*. Sea Dwelling Creatures, L.A., CA.

211

Astropecten

Common Name: Spiny Sand Star, Sand Sifting Star.

Region: Circumtropical.

Description: Flattened with prominent, tile-like plates and lateral spines along the margins of the arms. Tube feet with pointed tips (no suction cups). Found on sandy or muddy bottoms where they burrow in the substrate in search of food. Very active and effective sand movers in a reef aquarium.

Similar: *Iconaster*

Desirable/undesirable features: Ornamental. Useful in reef aquariums. Reef safe.

Food: Omnivore. Clams, worms, algae, detritus and microorganisms.

Special considerations: Keep with a deep sand bed. Offer dried seaweed (Nori) or small bits of clam meat. Without supplemental feeding they starve.

Hardiness in captivity: Hardy. Life span - years if fed properly.

Astropecten sp. from Fiji.

Iconaster

Common Name: None

Region: Red Sea to Western Pacific

Description: Large square tile-like marginal plates on the arms are light and dark, giving a banded appearance. The disc has more rounded plates of a darker color than the marginal plates. Found on coral rubble on reef slopes.

Similar: *Astropecten*

Desirable/undesirable features: Ornamental. Reef safe. May be harmful to some invertebrates, such as clams or sponges.

Food: May feed on small encrusting sponges. Offer mollusk meat.

Special considerations: Sensitive to changes in specific gravity, temperature, pH and oxygen levels and may succumb to bacterial infections that cause necrosis of the legs or whole body. Keep with live rock.

Hardiness in captivity: Delicate. Life span - months.

Iconaster longimanus from Singapore, Kenny Tan.

Tosia and *Pentagonaster*

Common Name: Red Biscuit Star.

Region: Temperate regions of the western Pacific.

Description: Large red or orange squarish marginal scales and red or orange circular scales on the rest of the dorsoventrally flattened surface. In between the tile-like scales there is white or yellow "grout" lines. *Tosia queenslandensis* is smaller and with shorter arms than *Pentagonaster duebeni*, but otherwise similar in appearance.

Similar: *Fromia* spp.

Desirable/undesirable features: Ornamental. Reef safe. May be harmful to some invertebrates, such as sponges.

Food: May feed on small encrusting sponges and bryozoans, in addition to bacterial films on live rock.

Special considerations: These seastars are from temperate regions and are stressed by water temperatures above 72 degrees F. Maintain in a chilled aquarium. Extremely sensitive to changes in specific gravity, temperature, pH and oxygen levels encountered during shipping, and usually succumb to rapid bacterial infections that cause necrosis of the legs or whole body. Keep with live rock, from which they graze.

Hardiness in captivity: Delicate. Life span - days - months.

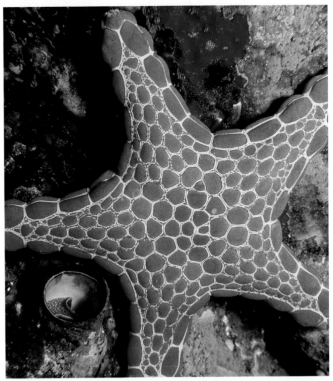

Orange *Pentagonaster duebeni* from Southern Australia. Carol Buchanan.

Red *Pentagonaster duebeni* from Southern Australia. Carol Buchanan.

213

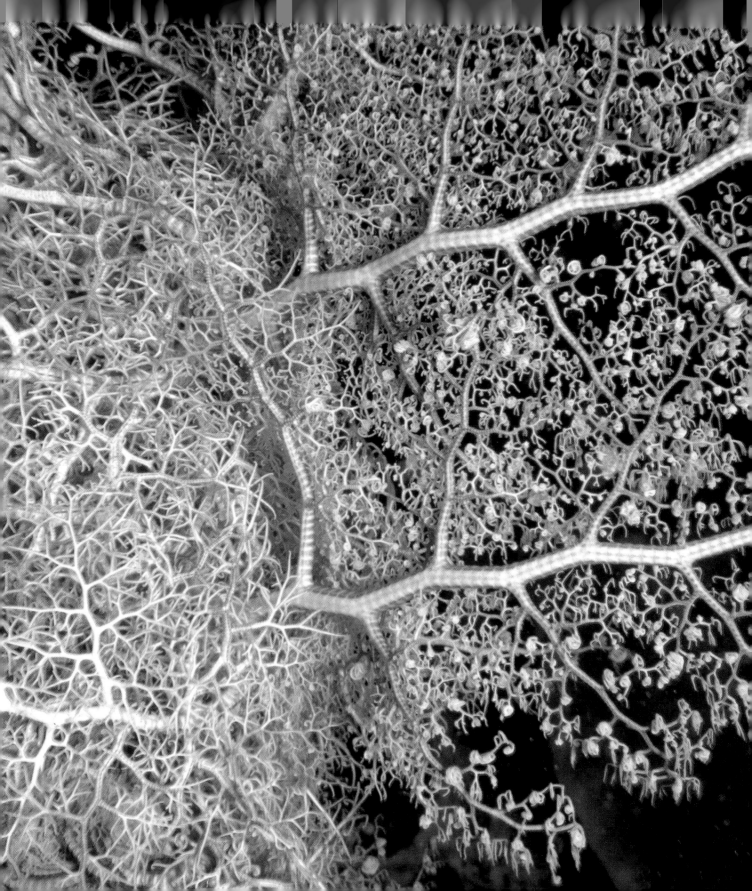

Astroboa, *Astrocaneum* and *Astrophyton*

Common Name: Basket Star.

Region: Circumtropical.

Description: Strange relatives of serpent stars, with highly branched arms used for snaring zooplankton. They remain in the reef, under corals, or at the base of gorgonians with arms folded during the day. At night they unfurl the arms and climb to an exposed perch to catch plankton.

Similar: *Schizostella bifurcata*, the Sea Rod Basket Star, a small species found curled around gorgonian branches.

Desirable/undesirable features: Ornamental. Reef safe.

Food: Carnivorous. Feeds on zooplankton and particulate organic matter.

Special considerations: Provide strong water currents and a prominent object projecting into the water stream (such as a gorgonian or coral branch). Feed enriched live *Artemia* (brine shrimp), *Gammarus*, worms, *Mysis*, frozen zooplankton, and marine snow at night when the aquarium lights are off and the arms are expanded. A dosing pump on a timer could be used to feed live brine shrimp this way.

Hardiness in captivity: Hardy when fed daily. Life span - months - years.

Basket star, *Astroboa* sp. feeding on zooplankton at night in the Solomon Islands.

215

Ophioderma and *Ophiolepis*

Common Name: Serpent Star, Red (Bahama) Serpent Star, Harlequin Serpent Star.

Region: Circumtropical.

Description: Smooth but scaly legs, often with bright color or banding. Common underneath rocks in sandy regions between reefs. *Ophioderma rubicundum* has maroon and white banding and very long thin legs. *Ophioderma squamosissimus* is the popular Red (Bahama) Serpent Star and it is a giant, attaining arm spans over 16 inches. Other species include *O. apressum*, *O. ensiferum*, *O. brevicaudum*, and *O. brevispinum*. *Ophiolepis superba* is light tan with dark brown bands on the arms and a variable pattern of dark markings on the disk. The legs are stiff and scaly.

Similar: *Ophiarachnella*, and *Ophioplocus*

Desirable/undesirable features: Ornamental. Useful in reef aquariums. Reef safe.

Food: Carnivorous. Detritivore. Scavenger that feeds on fish feces, dead organisms, and uneaten food.

Special considerations: Sensitive to changes in specific gravity, temperature, pH and oxygen levels encountered during shipping, and may succumb to rapid bacterial infections that cause necrosis of the legs or whole body. Keep in populations as high as one per five gallons (or this number in total when combined with other serpent star species) for effective scavenging of fish waste.

Hardiness in captivity: Hardy. Life span - years.

Ophiolepis superba is an attractive, hardy serpent star from Indonesia.

Ophioderma appressum has a variable color pattern. This harlequin form is most attractive. Florida.

Ophioderma squamosissimus from Florida.

Ophionereis

Common Name: Reticulated Brittle Star.

Region: Circumtropical.

Description: Common resident under rocks. Flattened with a reticulated pattern on the disc and banded cream-colored long slender arms. Edges of arms have spines. Tube feet used for walking, food transport, or movement of sand grains from.

Similar: *Ophiactis* spp. and *Ophiopsila* spp. The latter genus has species that put on a "fireworks display" at night. In the dark their arms become luminescent when disturbed, looking like blue lightning.

Desirable/undesirable features: Ornamental. Useful in reef aquariums. Reef safe.

Food: Carnivorous. Detritivore. Scavenger that feeds on fish feces, dead organisms, and uneaten food.

Special considerations: Provide sand or gravel and rocks.

Hardiness in captivity: Growth and reproduction. Life span - years.

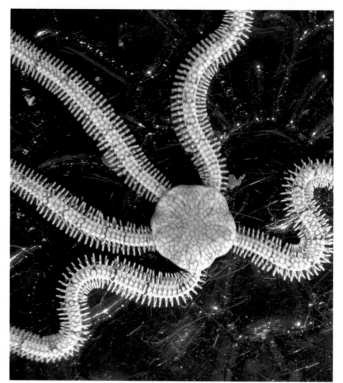

Ophionereis reticulata from Florida.

Ophiocoma

Common Name: Black Serpent Star, Black Brittle Star

Region: Circumtropical

Description: Black or brown spiny-legged serpent star. Arm span to over 12 inches. *Ophiocoma wendti* has red pigment on the underside, and small specimens have red spines. *Ophiocoma echinata* has shorter spines and is brownish. At night both species become paler and develop bands on the arms. *Ophiocoma aethiops* is the Eastern Pacific species.

Similar: *Ophiarachna* and *Ophiomastix*.

Desirable/undesirable features: Ornamental. Useful in reef aquariums. Reef safe*.

Food: Carnivorous. Detritivore. Scavenger that feeds on fish feces, dead organisms, and uneaten food.

Special considerations: *Reported to occasionally eat soft coral polyps or pester giant clams, but normally harmless.

Hardiness in captivity: Hardy. Life span - years.

Ophiocoma echinata from the Caribbean.

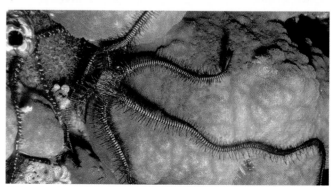

Ophiomastix variabilis. Solomon Islands.

Ophiarachna and **Ophiomastix**

Common Name: Brittle Star.

Region: Indo-Pacific.

Description: *Ophiarachna* is greenish or yellowish and has very spiny arms. It preys on small fishes that it traps at night. *Ophiomastix* has very elongate arms with short paddle-shaped spines on the margins of the arms mixed among shorter more numerous sharp spines.

Similar: *Ophiocoma*

Desirable/undesirable features: Ornamental. Useful in reef aquariums. Reef safe. Harmful to fishes.

Food: Carnivorous. Detritivore. Scavenger. Feed on fish feces, dead organisms, uneaten food. Traps and eats fish at night.

Special considerations: May trap gobies and other small or sluggish fishes. Dangerous to house with small fishes.

Hardiness in captivity: Hardy. Life span - years. *Ophiarachna incrassata* has reproduced in captivity. Reddish offspring grow without special feeding efforts by the aquarist.

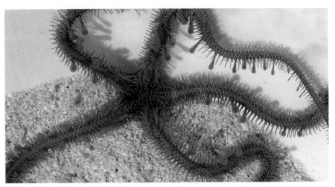
Ophiarachna incrassata is hardy but is a voracious fish predator, not safe with small fishes!

Ophiomastix annulosa from Indonesia.

Ophiothrix

Common Name: Sponge Brittle Star

Region: Circumtropical

Description: Elongate spiny arms wrapped around the branch of a gorgonian, sponge, or stony coral. Smaller species common on sponges underneath large flat rocks.

Similar: *Ophiarachna*, *Ophiomastix*

Desirable/undesirable features: Ornamental. Reef safe.

Food: Carnivorous. Detritivore. Feeds on zooplankton and particulate organic matter (marine snow). Will accept flake food and liquid invertebrate foods with large particle sizes.

Special considerations: Provide sponges or gorgonians for it to perch on, and maintain with a steady moderate to strong water current. Feed often. Sensitive to changes in specific gravity, temperature, pH and oxygen levels encountered during shipping, and may succumb to rapid bacterial infections that cause necrosis of the legs or whole body.

Hardiness in captivity: Delicate. Life span - years.

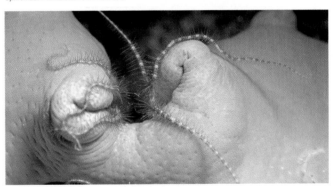
Ophiothrix sp. on a *Sarcophyton* sp. Leather Coral. Solomon Islands.

Ophiothrix sp. on Blue *Acropora*. Display aquarium at Reef and Fin, Connecticut.

Nemaster, Comantheria, Comanthina, Comanthus, Comaster, Comatula, Comissa, Decametra, Lamprometra, Oxycomanthus, Stephanometra, Petasometra and others

Common Name: Crinoid, Feather Star.

Region: Circumtropical and in temperate seas.

Description: Numerous colorful feather-shaped arms and (usually but not always) root-like legs called cirri. Some species are nocturnal. Feed on tiny zooplankton and drifting organic particles (marine snow) in exposed areas with moderate to swift water currents. Most species do not fare well in aquariums.

Similar: May be confused with Basket stars, or *Ophiothrix* spp. brittle stars.

Desirable/undesirable features: Ornamental. Reef safe.

Food: Carnivorous. Detritivore. Feeds on minute zooplankton of a narrow size range and particulate organic matter (marine snow).

Special considerations: Provide a steady moderate to strong water current. Feed often. Sensitive to changes in specific gravity, temperature, pH and oxygen levels encountered during shipping, and may succumb to rapid bacterial infections that cause necrosis of the legs or whole body. Starvation causes them to sever sections of the arm.

Hardiness in captivity: Most species are extremely delicate and not possible to maintain by the average or advanced aquarist. Life span - weeks - months. There have nevertheless been reports of success for years with a few species.

Comanthina sp. Solomon Islands.

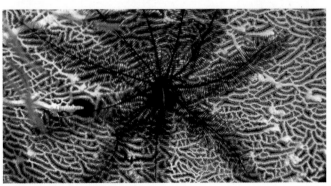

Colobometra perspinosa. Solomon Islands.

Stephanometra sp. Solomon Islands.

Oxycomanthus bennettii. Solomon Islands. Note "marine snow" on the arms.

221

Tunicates

Tunicates are invertebrates that belong to the phylum Chordata, the same phylum to which we human vertebrates belong. While vertebrates have a "backbone" or nerve cord, tunicates lack this feature in their adult form. The tiny or microscopic larvae of tunicates look very diferent from the adults, however, having a tadpole-shape and a distinct notochord. Of the three classes of tunicates, Acidiacea, Larvacea, and Thaliacea, the latter two are planktonic creatures not presently maintained in aquariums. The Acidiacea include the familiar "sea-squirts" and the majority of species.

A tunicate's body is covered with a thick "tunic" envelope composed of water, proteins and polysaccharides. The tunic is a living external skeleton with supportive and protective functions, and root like extensions of the basal part of the tunic attach the tunicate to the substrate. Often a fibrous component of the tunic is made of a type of cellulose called tunicin. A special feature of tunicates is their ability to concentrate and store trace elements from seawater, or produce biologically active chemical compounds that have potential use as antiviral or anti-cancer drugs.

Tunicates are filter feeders. A water current enters through a buccal siphon and exits through an atrial siphon in the simplest aspect of the "sea-squirt" body plan. In between the siphons it passes through a sieve-like pharyngeal basket, where the food is trapped. The water current is generated by cilia lining the lateral margins of a multitude of perforations or slits called stigmata that make the pharynx look like a sieve. The ribs between the pharyngeal slits of the basket are coated by a mucus secretion composed of iodine bound to the amino acid tyrosine. Frontal cilia on the ribs carry the mucus as a sheet across the pharynx, thus providing a continuously renewed surface for trapping food from the water passing through. The mucus film has a mesh-like ultrastructure that can trap particles as small as 0.1 µm. Digestion of the food occurs in a stomach and intestine. The food includes tiny plankton and particulate or dissolved organic matter, but carnivorous predatory species exist in deep water. In addition, tropical reefs feature tunicates with symbiotic algae (*Prochloron* spp.). As in corals, the host utilizes the photosynthetic products of the algae as food.

Individual tunicates can live for years, but many species have natural life spans of only several months. Most are hermaphroditic, and many reproduce vegetatively by budding. Some species reproduce in aquariums, but most just survive their natural lifespan of one year or less.

Polycarpa

Common Name: Sea Squirt.

Region: Circumtropical and in temperate seas.

Description: Members of this genus have the typical "sea squirt" shape. Most are large and solitary, though they may occur in groups, and a few species are colonial. The tunic is thick and leather-like, or slippery in some species. The color of the tunic is variable, often colorful. In some cryptic species the tunic is so obscured by epizoic growths that the tunicate appears to be a rock.

Similar: *Herdmania*

Desirable/undesirable features: Ornamental. Reef safe.

Food: Filter feeder.

Special considerations: Feed dissolved and particulate organic foods, bacteria or phytoplankton cultures. Supplement aquarium with iodine and trace elements.

Hardiness in captivity: Hardy. Life span - months.

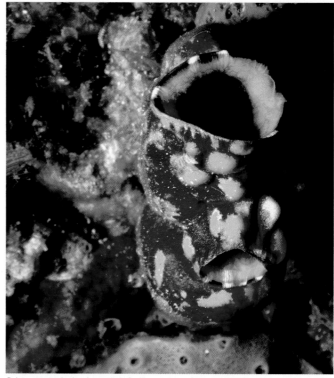

Polycarpa aurata is abundant on Indo-Pacific reef slopes. Solomon Islands.

Polycarpa aurata has variable color, normally in shades of purple, yellow, and white. Solomon Islands.

Clavelina

Common Name: Sea Squirt.

Region: Circumtropical.

Description: Colonies consist of a mass of club-shaped zooids attached on narrow stalks. The incurrent and excurrent siphons look like eyes or mouths. Often colorful in shades of yellow, green, orange, or blue.

Similar: *Pycnoclavella, Perophora, Diazona, Ecteinascidia,* and *Rhopalaea* spp.

Desirable/undesirable features: Ornamental. Reef safe.

Food: Filter feeder.

Special considerations: Provide strong water flow. Feed dissolved and particulate organic foods, bacteria or phytoplankton cultures. Supplement aquarium with iodine and trace elements.

Hardiness in captivity: Delicate. Life span - weeks - months.

Clavelina detorta from the Solomon Islands.

A choir of *Clavelina robusta* from the Solomon Islands.

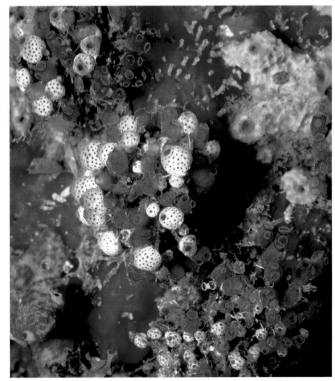

Blue *Clavelina* cf. *australis* with green *Didemnum molle* and sponges. Solomon Islands.

225

Didemnum

Common Name: Sea Squirt.

Region: Circumtropical.

Description: Encrusting or urn-shaped with a sponge-like appearance, having numerous tiny pores (the oral or in-current siphons) covering the surface in between the much larger few cloacal (ex-current) siphons. Some species, *D. molle* for example, harbor the symbiotic photosynthetic prokaryote *Prochloron*.

Similar: *Leptoclinides* and Trididemnum spp. resemble *Didemnum* spp.

Desirable/undesirable features: Ornamental. Reef safe.

Food: Filter feeder. Photosynthetic.

Special considerations: Provide strong illumination. Strong water flow. Feed dissolved and particulate organic foods, bacteria or phytoplankton cultures. Supplement aquarium with iodine and trace elements.

Hardiness in captivity: Hardy. Life span - months - years.

A red berry-like colonial tunicate, *Didemnum* cf. *moseleyi* on a reef slope in the Solomon Islands.

Didemnum molle, Solomon Islands. Note the bright green color of the symbiotic *Prochloron*.

Didemnum molle, Solomon Islands.

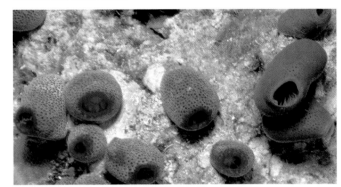

A cluster of *Didemnum molle*, Solomon Islands.

Variation of color in *Didemnum molle*, Solomon Islands.

Didemnum spp., other tunicates, sponges, soft corals, and hydroids on a current-swept reef wall in the Solomon Islands.

Botryllus and ***Botrylloides***

Common Name: Sea Squirt.

Region: Indo-Pacific, Caribbean.

Description: Low encrusting membranous colonial tunicates with very colorful diverse patterns like marble, paisley, or like psychedelic art. The zooids are arranged in rows, circles, or chains around volcano-like common excurrent siphons.

Similar: None.

Desirable/undesirable features: Ornamental. Reef safe.

Food: Filter feeder. Dissolved and fine particulate organic matter, bacteria.

Special considerations: Provide strong water flow. Feed dissolved and particulate organic foods, bacteria or phytoplankton cultures. Supplement aquarium with iodine and trace elements.

Hardiness in captivity: Hardy. Life span - months - years.

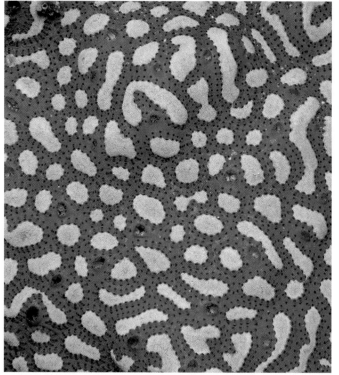

Botryllus sp. Solomon Islands.

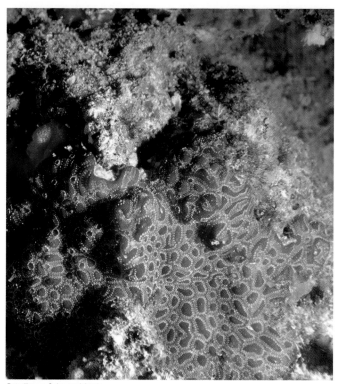

Botryllus sp. Solomon Islands.

228

Eudistoma

Common Name: Strawberry Tunicate.

Region: Circumtropical and in some temperate regions.

Description: *Eudistoma* spp. occur on hardbottoms near reefs, and some species can be found on mangrove roots. The zooids form a berry-like head on top of a thick stalk. In aquariums they may initially die back (the zooids shrink and disintegrate) leaving the thick hard base. After a few weeks new zooids arise and this tunicate blossoms into its former glory.

Similar: *Oxycorinia, Nephtheis, Sycozoa.*

Desirable/undesirable features: Ornamental. Reef safe.

Food: Filter feeder. Dissolved and fine particulate organic matter, bacteria.

Special considerations: Provide strong water flow. Feed dissolved and particulate organic foods, bacteria or phytoplankton cultures. Supplement aquarium with iodine and trace elements.

Hardiness in captivity: Hardy. Life span - months - years.

Nephtheis

Common Name: Lollipop Soft coral, Blue Cauliflower Sponge.

Region: Western Pacific.

Description: Green or blue smooth stalks with asparagus-like heads made up of clusters of zooids. Resemble nephtheid soft corals. Occur in current swept localities with organic matter in the water. In aquariums they may initially die back (the zooids shrink and disintegrate) leaving a thick hard base. After a few weeks, new zooids arise and this tunicate "blossoms" again.

Similar: *Eudistoma, Oxycorinia, Sycozoa*

Desirable/undesirable features: Ornamental. Reef safe.

Food: Filter feeder. Dissolved organic matter, bacteria.

Special considerations: Provide strong water flow. Feed dissolved and particulate organic foods, bacteria or phytoplankton cultures. Supplement aquarium with iodine and trace elements. Angelfish and Moorish Idols may eat them.

Hardiness in captivity: Hardy. Life span - months - years.

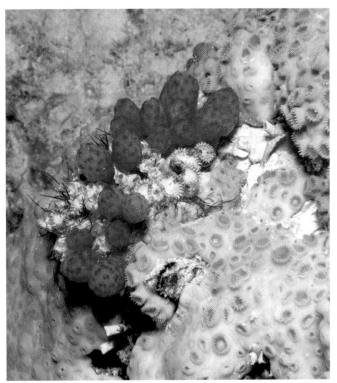

These "strawberry tunicates" *Eudistoma* sp. from Florida are both beautiful and hardy.

Blue *Nephtheis fascicularis* from Indonesia. Photographed at All Seas Fisheries, Miami Florida.

Nephtheis fascicularis from Indonesia. Photographed at All Seas Fisheries, Miami Florida.

abdomen - In crustaceans, the part of the body behind the cephalothorax.

aboral - the surface opposite from the mouth in sea stars, urchins, and other creatures.

acrosphere - Swelling at the tip of a tentacle, full of nematocysts.

aerole - feather-like crown of appendages used for feeding and respiration in "feather duster" annelid worms.

ambulacral groove - a furrow on the oral side of the arms of sea stars, from which the tube feet emerge.

annelid - worms with segmented bodies, belonging to the phylum Annelida.

anthozoan - members of the class Anthozoa, including anemones, corals, and jellyfish.

arborescent - tree-like, branching.

arthropod - animals in the phylum arthropoda, having an exoskeleton and jointed bodies and legs. eg. Crabs, lobsters, shrimps, amphipods, copepods, insects.

ascidian - a sea-squirt or tunicate.

asexual reproduction - vegetative reproduction including budding, fragmentation and fission, and spore formation. Reproduction not involving the union of gametes (sperm and egg).

atrium - the central exhalent water cavity in sponges, leading to one or many exhalent canals and pores (oscula). Frequently referred to incorrectly as cloaca.

benthic - living on or near the sea bottom.

bioluminescent - light production by living organisms.

bivalve - mollusks such as clams having two shells connected by a hinge.

buccal - oral, pertaining to the mouth.

budding - asexual reproduction by vegetative growth and formation of "buds," offspring that are also called propagules.

byssus filaments or **byssal threads** - tough thread-like filaments used by clams to attach to solid substrates and maintain position. Secreted by byssal gland.

calcareous - composed of calcium carbonate.

carapace - the region of the exoskeleton that covers the thorax in arthropods such as crabs and lobsters.

carnivore - feeds on animals.

cephalopod - octopus, squid, cuttlefish, nautilus, which belong to the class Cephalopoda.

cephalothorax - The head region in certain crustaceans, consisting of a dorsal carapace covering the thorax.

cf. - an abbreviation of "conferre," the Latin word meaning to compare. This is used with tentative species identifications, suggesting they should be compared with the formal description of the named species.

choanocytes - cells with a whip-like flagella that generate currents in sponges.

cilia - minute hair-like structures that serve as organs of locomotion or transport of food.

circumtropical - having a distribution around the world in tropical regions. For marine invertebrates this means the genus or species occurs in the Red Sea, Persian Gulf, Indian Ocean, Western Pacific, Pacific, Eastern Pacific, Caribbean, and Atlantic.

clavate - shaped like a club.

cnidaria - phylum that contains hydras, hydroids, jellyfish, sea anemones, and corals.

commensal - an animal that is living with or on another unrelated animal in a non-parasitic relationship.

conules - cone-shaped elevations of a sponge's surface membrane.

corallimorpharia - order of zoantharia closely related to corals, commonly called "mushroom anemones" or "false corals."

cryptic - hidden by having a dark and usually mottled color that tends to camouflage the outline and appearance of the creature, or covered by encrusting organisms to the same effect.

dichotomous - as in the letter y, the point of division produces two branches.

digitate - having finger-like lobes.

digitiform - a colony that is unbranched but finger-like in shape.

dimorphic - having two different forms.

divaricate - branching.

distal - the outermost part

ecosystem - all the organisms in a biotic community and the abiotic environmental factors they interact with.

ephyrae - larval jellyfish shaped like small medusae with lappets.

epizoic - (epizooic) types of animals or plants growing on the surface of other animals.

exudates - dissolved organic substances produced by an animal or plant and released into its surroundings. Such substances may be utilized as food by commensal organisms or may be used to attract or deter other creatures, or deter predation.

fecal pellet - the feces of many marine organisms, particularly of herbivores, are formed into lightweight pellets by their digestive systems.

foliaceous - shaped like a leaf.

genus - a grouping of related species with common characteristics.

glomerate - sphere-shaped.

herbivore - feeds on plant material

hydrostatic skeleton - a structural support against which the muscular system can act, provided by control of water pressure.

lobate - consisting of several stout lobes.

marine snow - particulate aggregates of organic matter drifting in the water column, formed by the release of dissolved organic substances in the water and subsequent chemical physical and biological reactions with them. Also includes the discarded "skins" of planktonic creatures, mineral clays and detritus. A very important food source for filter feeding invertebrates.

massive - having a solid lump-like shape.

mantle - the flap-like tissue in mollusks that secretes the calcareous shell. In giant clams the mantle harbors the symbiotic zooxanthellae.

medusa - a bell-shaped swimming stage of some types of cnidaria, i.e. jellyfish and hydrozoans. Anemones and corals do not have a medusa stage.

monomorphic - possessing just one form.

monotypic - a genus containing only one species.

notochord - a dorsal nerve chord (primitive backbone) found in larval tunicates that demonstrates their relation to vertebrates.

nematocyst - microscopic stinging body composed of a capsule containing an ejectable harpoon. Used for prey capture, attachment to substrate, and defense.

omnivore - feeds on both animal & plant material.

operculum - the door-like plate used by gastropod mollusks to shut the shell opening.

osculum - (oscule) - the large pore from which water exits the central cavity in many sponges (plural: oscula).

ostia - inhalent or incurrent openings (pores) through which water enters the sponge

palmate - shaped like a hand

pedicelariae - in sea urchins, forms of tube feet that have claw-like tips, used to hold or remove surface debris and sometimes venomous and used for defense.

photosynthesis - the process by which plants use light energy to make food.

photosynthetic - able to make food by photosynthesis. Corals have tiny plants called zooxanthellae living within their tissues, and so together they are called photosynthetic.

phytoplankton - microscopic algae suspended in the part of the water column that is penetrated by light. The foundation of aquatic food chains.

pinnules - side branches on the arms of crinoids that make them look like feathers. Also the side branches on soft coral tentacles.

plankton - animals, plants, larvae, and organic matter floating freely in the water and carried by the tides.

polyp - basic living unit of a coral or anemone.

porifera - phylum of sponges.

pleopod - see swimmeret.

pseudopodia - finger or hair-like extensions in ameba and forams, used for feeding and locomotion.

radula - file-like tooth apparatus used by many mollusks for rasping and chewing food.

reticulopodia - interconnected branches of hair-like pseudopodia in foraminiferans.

rhinophores - paired sensory tentacles or "antennae" found on the heads of seaslugs.

rostrum - a unicorn-like projection from the carapace in lobsters and shrimps.

salp - free-swimming species of tunicates, class Thaliacea.

sessile - attached to the substrate.

setae - short bristles found on annelid worms.

siphon - tube-like construction of tissue through which currents of water pass, as in sponges, tunicates, and mollusks.

spicule - sclerite. A skeletal element in soft corals composed of calcium carbonate. In sponges similar skeletal elements may be composed of silicon dioxide.

spongin - proteinaceous material that forms a mesh-like skeleton matrix in many sponges.

stolon - ribbon or root-like growth extensions that adhere to the substrate linking adjacent polyps or colonies.

strobilation - the process of forming and releasing larval medusae (ephyrae) from the polyp stage (scyphistoma) of jellyfish. It involves transverse fission of the oral end of the polyp.

sweeper tentacle - elongated tentacles of polyps that have increased numbers of nematocysts and can be used in aggressive encounters with neighbors.

swimmeret - (pleopod) one of several paired branched appendages found on the underside of the abdomen of shrimps and lobsters. Females carry eggs on these.

tentacles - thin finger-like (feather-like in soft corals) appendages with functions including prey capture, defense, gas exchange, locomotion, sensory, reproduction and light absorption.

test - the calcareous skeletal box made up of several sutured plates in sea urchins.

tube feet - The suction-cup-like extensions of the water vascular system in echinoderms such as sea urchins, seastars, and sea cucumbers, used for locomotion.

tubercles - wart-like projections.

tunic - a living external skeleton with supportive and protective functions in tunicates. It is composed of water, proteins and polysaccharides and, in many tunicates a fibrous component of the tunic is made of a type of cellulose called tunicin.

turbidity - reduced clarity in water. Usually caused by suspended organic or inorganic particles.

umbellate - shaped like an umbrella.

ventral - the underside.

verrucae - wart-like bumps on the column of sea anemones.

whorl - the spiral shape of a mollusk shell.

zoanthids - small anemone-like anthozoans with no skeleton; solitary or colonial e.g. *Palythoa*, *Parazoanthus* and *Zoanthus*.

zooplankton - animals that drift in the water column. Most are microscopic. Some are larval forms of larger organisms.

zooxanthellae - these are the tiny dinoflagellates that live symbiotically with corals, anemones, tridacnid clams, and some sponges, providing food to their host and in return getting the nitrogen, phosphorous and carbon dioxide they need for growth. *Symbiodinium* spp.

Abbott, R.T. and S. P. Dance (1998) *Compendium of Seashells*. Odyssey Publishing. El Cajon, CA. 411 pp.

Albani, A. D. (1968) Recent Foraminiferida of the central coast of New South Wales. *Australian Marine Sciences Association Handbook* 1: 1-37.

Ahyong, S. (1977) Phylogenetic analysis of the stomatopoda (Malacostraca). *Jour. Crust. Biol.* 17 (4): 695-715.

Allen, G. R. & R. Steene (1994) *Indo-Pacific Coral Reef Field Guide*. Tropical Reef Research, Singapore.

Arai, M. N. and Walder, G. L. (1973) The feeding response of *Pachycerianthus fimbriatus* (Ceriantharia). *Comp. Biochem. Physiol.*, 44A, 1085-1092.

Arnold, P. W. and Birtles, R. A. (1989) *Soft Sediment marine invertebrates of southeast Asia and Australia: a guide to identification*. Australian Institute of Marine Science: Townsville, 272 pp.

Ayre, D. J. (1983) The effects of asexual reproduction and inter-genotypic aggression on the genotypic structure of populations of the sea anemone *Actinia tenebrosa*. *Oecologia*, 57, 158-165.

Ayre, D. J. (1984) The sea anemone *Actinia tenebrosa*: an opportunistic insectivore. *Ophelia*, 23, 149-153.

Ayre, D. J. (1985) Localized adaptation of clones of the sea anemone *Actinia tenebrosa*. *Evolution*, 39, 1250-1260.

Ayre, D. J. (1987) The formation of clonal territories in experimental populations of the sea anemone *Actinia tenebrosa*. *Biol. Bull.*, 172, 178-186.

Ayre, D. J. (1988) Evidence for genetic determination of sex in *Actinia tenebrosa*. *J. Exp. Mar. Biol. Ecol.*, 116, 23-34.

Bach, C. E. and Herrnkind, W. F. (1980) Effects of predation pressure on the mutualistic interaction between the hermit crab, *Pagurus pollicaris* Say, 1817, and the sea anemone, *Calliactis tricolor* (Lesueur, 1817). *Crustaceana*, 38, 104-108.

Balasch, J. and Mengual, V. (1974) The behaviour *of Dardanus arrosor* in association with *Calliactis parasitica* in artificial habitat. *Mar. Behav. Physiol.*, 2, 251-260.

Barnes, R. D. (1987) *Invertebrate Zoology*, Fifth Edition. CBS College Publishing. 893 pp.

Barnes, R. S. K., Calow, P. and Olive, P. J. W. (1988) *The Invertebrates, A new Synthesis*. Blackwell Scientific Publications.

Benson-Rodenbough, B. and Ellington, W. R. (1982) Responses of the euryhaline sea anemone *Bunodosoma cavernata* (Bosc) (Anthozoa, Actiniaria, Actiniidae) to osmotic stress. *Comp. Biochem. Physiol.*, 72A, 731-735.

Bernheimer, A. W. and Avigad, L. S. (1976) Properties of a toxin from the sea anemone *Stoichactis helianthus*, including specific binding to sphingomyelin. *Proc. Nat. Acad. Sci.* USA, 73, 467-471.

Bergquist, P. R. (1978) *Sponges*. Hutchinson: London, pp. 1-268.

Bergquist, P. R., Ayling, A. M. and Wilkinson, C. R. (1988) Foliose Dictyoceratida of the Australian Great Barrier Reef. 1. Taxonomy and phylogenetic relationships. *Mar. Ecol.* 9(4): 291-320.

Bishop, S. H., Ellis, L. L. and Burcham, J. M. (1983) Amino acid metabolism in molluscs. In P. W. Hochachka (ed.), *The Mollusca*. Vol. 1. Metabolic Biochemistry and Molecular Biomechanics, Academic Press, New York, pp. 243-327.

Black, R. and Johnson, M. S. (1979) Asexual viviparity and population genetics of *Actinia tenebrosa*. *Mar. Biol.*, 53, 27-31.

Boury-Esnault, N. and Doumenc, D. A. (1979) Glycogen storage and transfer in primitive invertebrates: Demospongea and Actiniaria. In C. Levi and N. Boury-Esnault (eds.), *Biologie des Spongiaires*, Colloques Internationaux du CNRS No. 291, Centre National de la Recherche Scientifique, Paris, pp. 181-192.

Brace, R. C. and Quicke, D. L. J. (1986) Dynamics of colonization by the beadlet anemone, *Actinia equina*. *J. Mar. Biol. Ass. UK*, 66, 21-47.

Brace, R.C. and Reynolds, H.A. (1989) Relative intraspecific aggressiveness of pedal disc colour phenotypes of the beadlet anemone, *Actinia equina*. *J. Mar. Biol. Ass. UK*, 69, 273-278.

Brooks, W. R. (1989a) Hermit crabs alter sea anemone placement patterns for shell balance and reduced predation. *J. Exp. Mar. Biol. Ecol.*, 132, 109-122.

Brooks, W. R. (1989b) Hermit crabs protect their symbiotic cnidarians-true cases of mutualism. *Amer. Zool.*, 29, 36A (abstract).

Brooks, W. R. and Mariscal, R. N. (1984) The acclimation of anemone fishes to sea anemones: protection by changes in the fish's mucous coat. *J. Exp. Mar. Biol. Ecol.*, 81, 277-285.

Brooks, W. R. and Mariscal, R. N. (1986a) Interspecific competition for space by hydroids and a sea anemone living on gastropod shells inhabited by hermit crabs. *Mar. Ecol. Prog. Ser.*, 28, 241-244.

Brooks, W. R. and Mariscal, R. N. (1986b) Population variation and behavioral changes in two pagurids in association with the sea anemone *Calliactis tricolor* (Leseur). *J. Exp. Mar. Biol. Ecol.*, 103, 275-289.

Bruce, A. J. (1976) Shrimps and prawns of coral reefs, in O. A. Jones and R. Endean (eds.) *Biology and Geology of Coral Reefs*, Vol III. Academic Press, New York. Pp. 37-94.

Bullock, T. H. and Horridge, G. A. (1965) Coelenterata and Ctenophora. In T.H. Bullock and G.A. Horridge, *Structure and Function in the Nervous Systems of Invertebrates*, Vol. I, W.H. Freeman, San Francisco, pp. 459-534.

Babcock, R. C. and Ryland, J. S. (1990) Larval development of a tropical zoanthid (*Protopalythoa* sp.). *Invert. Reprod. Develop.* 17: 229-236.

Bursey, C. R. and Guanciale, J. M. (1977) Feeding behavior of the sea anemone *Condylactis gigantea*. *Comp. Biochem. Physiol.*, 57A, 115-117.

Bursey, C. R. and Harmer, J. A. (1979) Induced changes in the osmotic concentration of the coelenteron fluid of the sea anemone *Condylactis gigantea*. *Comp. Biochem. Physiol.*, 64A, 73-76.

Buss, L. W., McFadden, C. S. and Keene, D. R. (1984) Biology of hydractiniid hydroids. 2. Histocompatibility effector system/competitive mechanism mediated by nematocyst discharge. *Biol. Bull.*, 167, 139-158.

Cairns, S., Hartog, J. C. den and Arneson, C. (1986) Class Anthozoa (Corals, anemones). In W. Sterrer (ed.), *Marine Fauna and Flora of Bermuda. A Systematic Guide to the Identification of Marine Organisms*, John Wiley & Sons, New York, pp. 159-194.

Calow, P. (1981) Growth in lower invertebrates. In M. Rechcigl (ed.), Physiology of Growth and Nutrition, S. Karger, Basel, pp. 53-76.

Cannon, L. R. G., 1986. *Turbellaria of the World: a guide to the families and genera*. Queensland Museum, Bisbane, Australia. 136 pp.

Carlgren, O. (1949) A survey of the Ptychodactiaria, Corallimorpharia and Actiniaria. *Kungl. Sven. Vetenskapsakad. Handlingar, Ferde Ser.*, 1, 1-121 + 4 plates.

Carter, M. A. and Funnell, M. (1980) Reproduction and brooding in *Actinia*. In P. Tardent and R. Tardent (eds.), *Developmental and Cellular Biology of Coelenterates*, North-Holland Biomedical Press, Amsterdam, pp. 17-22.

Carter, M. A. and Miles, J. (1989) Gametogenic cycles and reproduction in the beadlet sea anemone *Actinia equina* (Cnidaria: Anthozoa). *Biol. J. Linn. Soc.*, 36, 129-155.

Cates, N. and McLaughlin, J.J.A. (1976) Differences of ammonia metabolism in symbiotic and aposymbiotic *Condylactus* and *Cassiopea* spp. *J., Exp. Mar. Biol. Ecol.*, 21, 1-5.

Cates, N. and McLaughlin, J. J. A. (1979) Nutrient availability for zooxanthellae derived from physiological activities of *Condylactus* spp. *J. Exp. Mar. Biol. Ecol.*, 37, 31-41.

Chadwick, N. E. (1987) Interspecific aggressive behavior of the corallimorpharian *Corynactis californica* (Cnidaria: Anthozoa): effects on sympatric corals and sea anemones. *Biol. Bull.*, 173, 110-125.

Clark, A. M. and F. W. E. Rowe (1971) *Monograph of Shallow Water Indo-West Pacific Echinoderms*. British Museum of Natural History, London.

Coleman, N. (1989) *Nudibranchs of the South Pacific Sea*. Australian Resource Center: Springwood, Qld.

Colin, P. L. and C. Arneson. (1995) *Tropical Pacific Invertebrates. A Field Guide to the Marine Invertebrates Occurring on Tropical Pacific Coral Reefs, Seagrass Beds, and Mangroves*. Coral Reef Press, Beverly Hills, CA.

Conklin, E. J. and Mariscal, R. N. (1977) Feeding behavior, ceras structure, and nematocyst storage in the aeolid nudibranch, *Spurilla neapolitana* (Mollusca). *Bull. Mar. Sci.*, 27, 658-667.

Cutress, C. E. (1979) *Bunodeopsis medusoides* Fowler and *Actinodiscus neglectus* Fowler, two Tahitian sea anemones: redescription and biological notes. *Bull. Mar. Sci.*, 29, 96-109.

Davey, K. (1998) *A Photographic Guide to Seashore Life of Australia*. New Holland Publishers, Sydney, Australia. 144 pp.

Debelius, H. (1983) *Armoured Knights of the Sea*. Kernen Verlag, Essen, 120 pp.

Debelius, H. (1999) *Crustacea Guide of The World*. IKAN - Unterwasserarchiv, Frankfurt, Germany. 321 pp.

Delbeek, J. C. and J. Sprung (1994) *The Reef Aquarium*, Volume one. Ricordea Publishing, Miami Florida. 546 pp.

Dunn, D. F. (1981) The clownfish sea anemones: Stichodactylidae (Coelenterata: Actiniaria) and other sea anemones symbiotic with pomacentrid fishes. *Trans. Amer. Phil. Soc.*, 71, 1-115.

Dunn, D. F. and Hamner, W. M. (1980) *Amplexidiscus fenestrafer* n. gen, n. sp. (Coelenterata: Anthozoa), a tropical Indo-Pacific corallimorpharian. *Micronesica*, 16, 29-36.

Ellington, W. R. (1982) Metabolic responses of the sea anemone *Bunodosoma cavernata* (Bosc) to declining oxygen tensions and anoxia. *Physiol. Zool.*, 55, 240-249.

Elliott, J. and Cook, C. B. (1989) Diel variation in prey capture behavior by the corallimorpharian *Discosoma sanctithomae*: mechanical and chemical activation of feeding. *Biol. Bull.*, 176, 218-228.

Erhardt, H. and Moosleitner, H. (1998) *Marine Atlas 3 Invertebrates*. Baensch, Melle Germany. 1326 pp.

Fauchaud, K. (1977) *The polychaete worms*. Natural History Museum of Los Angeles County, Science Series vol 28. 188 pp.

Fautin, D. G. (1986) Why do anemonefishes inhabit only some host actinians? *Envir. Biol. Fishes*, 15, 171-180.

Fautin, D. G., Spaulding, J. G. and Chia, F.-S. (1989) Cnidaria. In K. G. Adiyodi and R. G. Adiyodi (eds.), *Reproductive Biology of Invertebrates, Vol. IV, Fertilization, Development, and Parental Care*, Oxford and IBH Publishing Co., New Delhi, pp. 43-62.

Fautin, D. G. and G. Allen (1992) *Field Guide to Anemonefishes and Their Host Sea Anemones*. Western Australian Museum, Perth, W.A.

Fielding, A. and E. Robinson. (1987) *An Underwater Guide to Hawaii*. University of Hawaii Press, Honolulu, HI. 156 pp.

Fossá, S., and A. J. Nilsen. (1998) *The Modern Coral Reef Aquarium*, Volume 2. Birgit Schmettkamp Verlag, Bornheim, Germany. 479 pp.

Fossá, S., and A. J. Nilsen. (2000) *The Modern Coral Reef Aquarium*, Volume 3. Birgit Schmettkamp Verlag, Bornheim, Germany. 448 pp.

Friese, U. E. (1972) *Sea Anemones*, T.F.H. Publications, Neptune City, New Jersey, 128 pp.

Gammill, E. R. (1997) *Identification of Coral Reef Sponges*. Providence Marine Publishing. Tampa, 117 pp.

Gashout, S. E. and Ormond, R. F. G. (1979) Evidence for parthenogenetic reproduction in the sea anemone *Actinia equina* L. *J. Mar. Biol. Ass. UK*, 59, 975-987.

Gosliner, T.M. (1987) *Nudibranchs of Southern Africa. A Guide to Opisthobranch Molluscs of Southern Africa*. Sea Challengers, Monterey, California. 136 pp.

Gosliner, T.M. (1995) The Genus *Thuridilla* (Opisthobranchia: Elysiidae) from the Tropical Indo-Pacific, with a Revision of the Phylogeny and Systematics of the Elysiidae. *Proceedings of the Californian Academy of Sciences, 49(1)*:1-54.

Gosliner, T. M, Williams, G. C. and D. Behrens (1996) *Coral Reef Animals of the Indo Pacific*. Sea Challengers, Monterey, CA. 314 pp.

Greenwood, P. G. and Mariscal, R. N. (1984b) The utilization of cnidarian nematocysts by aeolid nudibranchs: nematocyst maintenance and release in *Spurilla*. *Tissue & Cell*,16, 719-730.

Guille, A., Laboute, P. and J.-L. Menou (1986) Guide des étoiles de mer, oursins et autres échinodermes du lagon de Nouvelle-Calédonie. Éditions de l'Orstom, Paris. 238 pp.

Haddon, A. C. (1895) Branched worm tubes and *Acrozoanthus. Scient. Proc. R. Dubl. Soc.*, N. S. 8:344-36

Hammond, L. S. and Wilkinson, C. R. (1985) Exploitation of Sponge Exudates by coral reef holothuroids. J. exp. Mar. Biol. Ecol. 94(1-3): 1-10.

Hamner, W. M. and Dunn, D. F. (1980) Tropical Corallimorpharia (Coelenterata: Anthozoa) feeding by envelopment. *Micronesica*, 16, 37-41.

Harbison, G.R. and Madin, L. P. (1982) Ctenophora. in S. P. Parker (ed) *Synopsis and Classification of Living Organisms*, McGraw-Hill, New York, pp. 707-715.

Harris, L. G. (1973) Nudibranch associations. In T. C. Cheng (ed.), *Current Topics in Comparative Pathobiology*, Vol. 2, Academic Press, New York, pp. 213-315.

Harris, L. G. (1987) Aeolid nudibranchs as predators and prey. *Amer. Malacol. Bull.*, 5, 287-292.

Hartog, J.C. DEN (1980) Caribbean Shallow Water Corallimorpharia. *Zoologische Verhandelingen*. (176): 1-83.

Hendler, G., Miller, J. E., Pawson, D. L., and Kier, P. M. (1996) *Sea Stars, Sea Urchins and Allies: Echinoderms of Florida and the Caribbean*. Smithsonian Institution Press.

Herberts, C. (1987) Ordre des Zoanthaires. in P.-P. Grasse (ed) *Traite de Zoologie*. Masson: Paris. Pp. 783-810.

Herndl, G. J., Velimirov, B. and Krauss, R. E. (1985) Heterotrophic nutrition and control of bacterial density in the coelenteron of the giant sea anemone *Stoichactis giganteum*. *Mar. Ecol. Prog. Ser.*, 22, 101-105.

Higgins, R. P. and Thiel, H. (1988*) Intoduction to the Study of Meiofauna*. Smithsonian Institution Press: Washington, 488 pp.

Humann, P. (1991) *Reef Creature Identification - Florida, Caribbean, Bahamas*. New World Publications. 344 pp.

Jennison, B. L. (1981) Reproduction in three species of sea anemones from Key West, Florida. *Can. J. Zool*, 59, 1708-1719.

Jensen, K.R. (1999) A new species of Sacoglossa (Mollusca, Opisthobranchia) from Rottnest Island, Western Australia. [In]: D.J.Walker & F.E.Wells (Eds). *The Seagrass Flora and Fauna of Rottnest Island, Western Australia*. Western Australian Museum, Perth: 377-383.

Kerstich, A. (1989) *Sea of Cortez Marine Invertebrates*. Sea Challengers. Monterey Ca. 114 pp.

Knop, D. (1996) *Giant Clams: A Comprehensive Guide to the Identification and Care of Tridacnid Clams*. Dähne Verlag, Ettlingen, Germany. 255 pp.

Knowlton, N. and Keller, B. D. (1986) Larvae which fall far short of their potential: highly localized recruitment in an alpheid shrimp with extended larval development. *Bull. Mar. Sci.*, 39, 213-223.

Koehl, M. A. R. (1977a) Effects of sea anemones on the flow forces they encounter. *J. Exp. Biol.*, 69, 87-105.

Koehl, M. A. R. (1977d) Water flow and the morphology of zoanthid colonies. In D. L. Taylor (ed.*), Proceedings of the Third International Coral Reef Symposium*, Vol. 1, Biology, Rosenstiel School of Marine and Atmospheric Science, University of Miami, Miami, Florida, pp. 438-444.

Kott, P. (1980) Algal bearing didemnid ascidians of the Indo-west Pacific. *Mem. Qd. Mus.* 20(1): 1-38.

Kott, P. (1981) The Ascidians of the Reef Flats of Fiji. *Proc. Linn. Soc. NSW* 105 (3): 147-212.

Kott, P., Parry, D. and Cox, G. C. (1984) Prokaryotic symbionts with a range of ascidian hosts. *Bull Mar. Sci.* 34: 308-312.

Lange, J. and R. Kaiser (1991) *Niedere Tiere tropischer und kalter Meere*. Eugen Ulmer GmbH, Stuttgart, Germany. 224 pp.

Lawrence, J. M. (1987) *A Functional Biology of Echinoderms*, Croom Helm, London, 340 pp.

Levi, C., Ed. (1998) *Sponges of the New Caledonian Lagoon*. Orstrom Editions, Paris. 214 pp.

Levine, D. M. and Blanchard, O. J., Jr. (1980) Acclimation of two shrimps of the genus *Periclimenes* to sea anemones. *Bull. Mar. Sci.*, 30, 460-466.

Lewis, J. B. (1984) Photosynthetic production by the coral reef anemone, Lebrunea coralligens Wilson, and behavioral correlates of two nutritional strategies. *Biol. Bull.*, 167, 601-612.

Limbaugh, C., Pederson, H. and Chace, F. A., Jr. (1961) Shrimps that clean fishes. *Bull. Mar. Sci.*, 11, 237-257.

Madrigal, L. G. (1999) *Field Guide of Shallow Water Marine Invertebrates of American Samoa*. Larry Madrigal, Pago Pago, American Samoa. 132 pp.

Manning, R. B. (1980) The Superfamilies, families, and genera of recent stomatopod Crustacea, with diagnoses of six new families. *Biol. Soc. Washington* 93(2): 362-372.

Manton, S. M. (1977) *The Arthropoda: Habits, Functional Morphology and Evolution*. Oxford University Press (Clarendon): London and New York.

Mariscal, R. N. (1970a) The nature of the symbiosis between Indo-Pacific anemone fishes and sea anemones. *Mar. Biol.*, 6, 58-65.

Mariscal, R. N., Conklin, E. J. and Bigger, C. H. (1977) The ptychocyst, a major new category of cnida used in tube construction by a cerianthid anemone. *Biol. Bull.*, 152, 392-405.

Mather, P. and I. Bennet. (eds.) (1993) Coral Reef Handbook, A guide to the geology, flora and fauna of the Great Barrier Reef. Surrey Beatty and Sons, Norton, NSW, Australia. 264 pp.

Mebs, D. (1989) *Gifte im Riff*. Wissenschaftliche Verlagsgesellschaft mbH, Stuttgart, Germany.

Monniot, C., Monniot, F. and P. Laboute (1991) Coral Reef Ascidians of New Caledonia, Editions de l'Orstom, Paris, 248 pp.

Moore, R. E. and Scheuer, P. J. (1971) Palytoxin: a new marine toxin from a coelenterate. *Science*, 172, 495-498.

Muirhead, A. and Ryland, J. S. (1985) A review of the genus *Isaurus* Gray, 1828 (Zoanthidea), including new records from Fiji. *J. nat Hist.* 19: 323-335.

Norman, M. (2000) *Cephalopods - A World Guide*. Conch Books. 320 pp.

Oglesby, L. C. (1975) An analysis of water-content regulation in selected worms. In F. J. Vernberg (ed.), *Physiological Ecology of Estuarine Organisms*, University of South Carolina Press, Columbia, pp. 181-204.

Ottaway, J. R. (1979) Population ecology of the intertidal anemone *Actinia tenebrosa* II. Geographical distribution, synonymy, reproductive cycle and fecundity. *Aust. J. Zool.*, 27, 273-290.

Patterson, M. R. (1985) *The Effects of Flow on the Biology of Passive Suspension Feeders: Prey Capture, Feeding Rate, and Gas Exchange in Selected Cnidarians*. Ph.D. dissertation, Harvard University, Cambridge, Massachusetts, 342 pp.

Pechenik, J. A. (1996). *Biology of the Invertebrates*. William C. Brown, Co. 553 pp.

Peteya, D. J. (1973) A possible proprioreceptor *in Ceriantheopsis americanus* (Cnidaria, Ceriantharia). *Z. Zellforsch.*, 144, 1-10.

Prudhoe, S. (1985) *A Monograph on Polyclad Turbellaria*. British Museum (NH): London, 259 pp.

Quicke, D. L. J. and Brace, R. C. (1983) Phenotypic and genotypic spacing within an aggregation of the anemone, *Actinia equina*. *J. Mar. Biol. Ass.* UK, 63, 493-515.

Ross, D. M. and Boletzky, S. von (1979) The association between the pagurid *Dardanus arrosor* and the actinian *Calliactis parasitica*. Recovery of activity in 'inactive' *D. arrosor* in the presence of cephalopods. *Mar. Behav. Physiol.*, 6, 175-184.

Rubenstein, D. I. and Koehl, M. A. R. (1977) The mechanisms of filter feeding: some theoretical considerations. *Amer. Nat.*, 111, 981-994.

Rudman, W.B., (1970) *Chelidonura inornata* Baba and C. *electra* sp. nov. from the Solomon Islands (Opisthobranchia, Aglajidae). *Journal of the Malacological Society, Australia*, 2: 7-12.

Rudman, W.B. (1986) The Chromodorididae (Opisthobranchia: Mollusca) of the Indo-West Pacific: *Noumea flava* colour group. *Zoological Journal of the Linnean Society* 88: 377-404.

Rudman, W.B., (1991a) Purpose in pattern: the evolution of colour in chromodorid nudibranchs. *J. Moll. Stud.* 57: 5-21

Rudman, W.B., (1991b) Further studies on the taxonomy and biology of the octocoral-feeding genus *Phyllodesmium* Ehrenberg, 1831 (Nudibranchia: Aeolidoidea). *J. Moll. Stud.* 57: 167-203.

Rudman, W.B., (2000, March 3) *Ercolania endophytophaga* Jensen, 1999. *[In] Sea Slug Forum.* http://seaslugforum.net/ercoendo.htm

Russell, F. E., and R. Nagabhushanam (1996) *The Venomous and Poisonous Marine Invertebrates of the Indian Ocean.* Science Publishers, Enfield, New Hampshire, USA. 271 pp.

Sassaman, C. and Mangum, C. P. (1974) Gas exchange in a cerianthid. *J. Exp. Zool.*, 188, 297-306.

Schiemer, G. (1994) Hermit Crabs in the Reef Aquarium. *Aquarium Frontiers.* Summer 1994: 4-5, 10-11.

Schlichter, D. (1980) Adaptations of cnidarians for integumentary absorption of dissolved organic matter. *Rev. Can. Biol.*, 39, 259-282.

Schlichter, D., Bajorat, K. H., Buck, M., Eckes, P., Gutknecht, D., Kraus, P., Krisch, H., and Schmitz, B. (1987) Epidermal nutrition of sea anemones by absorption of organic compounds dissolved in the oceans. *Zool. Beitr. N.F.*, 30, 29-47.

Schmidt, H. (1974) On evolution in the Anthozoa. In *Proceedings of the Second International Coral Reef Symposium*, Vol. 1, Great Barrier Reef Committee, Brisbane, Pp. 533-560.

Shick, J. M. (1975) Uptake and utilization of dissolved glycine by *Aurelia aurita* scyphistomae: Temperature effects on the uptake process; nutritional role of dissolved amino acids. *Biol. Bull.*, 148, 117-140.

Shick, J. M. (1983) Respiratory gas exchange in echinoderms. In M. Jangoux and J. M. Lawrence (eds.), *Echinoderm Studies*, Vol. 1, Balkema Publishers, Rotterdam, pp. 67-110.

Shick, J. M. (1990) Diffusion limitation and hyperoxic enhancement of oxygen consumption in zooxanthellate sea anemones, zoanthids, and corals. *Biol. Bull.*, 179, 148-158.

Shoup, J. B., (1968) Shell opening by crabs of the genus *Calappa. Science*, 160: 887-888.

Schuhmacher, H. (1977) A Hermit Crab, Sessile on Corals, Exclusively Feeds by Feathered Antennae. *Oecologia* (Berlin) 27: 371-374.

Snyderman, M. and C. Wiseman (1997). *Guide to Marine Life Caribbean, Bahamas, Florida* Aqua Quest. New York. 284 pp.

Sprung, J. and J. C. Delbeek (1997) *The Reef Aquarium*, Vol two. Ricordea Publishing, Miami Florida. 546 pp.

Steele, R. D. (1977) The significance of zooxanthella-containing pellets extruded by sea anemones. *Bull. Mar. Sci.*, 27, 591-594.

Steene, R. (1990) *Coral Reefs Natures Richest Realm.* Mallard Press, New York. 336 pp.

Steene, R. (1998) *Coral Seas.* Firefly Books. Buffalo, New York, USA. 271 pp.

Talbot, F. (ed), 1984. *Readers Digest Book of the Great Barrier Reef.* Readers Digest: Sydney.

Taylor, D. (1970) Photosynthesis of symbiotic chloroplasts in *Tridachia crispata* (Bergh). *Comparative Biochemistry and Physiology, 38A*: 233-236.

Tiffon, Y. and Bouillon, J. (1975) Digestion extracellulaire dans la cavite gastrique de *Cerianthus lloydi* Gosse. Structure du gastroderme, localisation et proprie e des enzymes proteolytiques. *J. Exp. Mar. Biol. Ecol.*, 18, 255-269.

Tiffon, Y. and Daireaux, M. (1974) Phagocytose et pinocytose par l'ectoderme et l'endoderme de *Cerianthus lloydi* Gosse. *J. Exp. Mar. Biol. Ecol.*, 16, 155-165.

Trench, R.K. (1969) Chloroplasts as functional endosymbionts in the mollusc *Tridachia crispata* (Bergh). *Nature*, 222: 1071-1072.

Trench, R. K. (1987) Dinoflagellates in non-parasitic symbioses. In F. J. R. Taylor (ed.), The Biology of Dinoflagellates. *Botanical Monographs*, No. 21, Blackwell Scientific Publications, Oxford, UK, pp. 530-570.

Tyree, S. (1998) *The Porifera (Living Sponges) - Their Biology, Physiology and natural Filtration Integration.* Volume 1 of the Captive Oceans Series. DE Publishing, 204 pp.

Van-Praet, M. (1983) Regime alimentaire des Actinies. *Bull. Soc. Zool. France*, 108, 403-407.

Verwey, J. (1930) Coral reef studies. I. The symbiosis between damselfishes and sea anemones in Batavia Bay. *Treubia*, 12, 305-366.

Werner, B. (1973) New investigations on systematics and evolution of the class Scyphozoa and the phylum Cnidaria. *Publ. Seto Mar. Biol. Lab.*, 20, 35-61.

Westheide, W. (1988) Polychaeta. In R. P. Higgins and H. Thiel, (eds.) *Intoduction to the Study of Meiofauna.* Smithsonian Institution Press: Washington, pp. 332-344.

Wilkens, P. (1980) *Niedere Tiere im tropischen Seewasser-Aquarium.* Vol 2. Engelbert Pfriem Verlag, Wuppertal, Germany

Wilkerson, F. P. and Muscatine, L. (1984) Uptake and assimilation of dissolved inorganic nitrogen by a symbiotic sea anemone. *Proc. R. Soc. Lond.*, B, 221, 71-86.

Wilkerson, J. D. Clownfishes, A Guide to Their Captive Care, Breeding & Natural History. Microcosm Ltd. Shelburne, VT. 240 pp.

Wilkinson, C. R. (1988) Foliose Dictyoceratida of the Australian Great Barrier Reef. 2. Ecology and duistribution of these prevalent sponges. *Mar. Ecol.* 9(4): 321-328.

Wilkinson, C. R. and Cheshire, A.C. (1989) Patterns in the distribution of sponge populations across the central Great Barrier Reef. *Coral Reefs* 8: 127-134.

Willan, R. C. and N. Coleman (1984) *Nudibranchs of Australasia.* Australasian Marine Photographic Index. Sydney, Australia.

Winsor, L. (1990) Marine Turbellaria (Acoela) from North Queensland. *Mem. Qd. Mus.* 28: 785-800.

Wood, R. (1990) Reef-building sponges. *American Scientist* 78: 224-35.

Wrobel, David and Claudia Mills, 1998. *Pacific Coast Pelagic Invertebrates.* Sea Challengers, Monterey California

Zea, S. (1987) *Esponjas del Caribe Colombiano.* Editorial Catalogo Scientifico, 286 pp.

Zwaan, A. de (1983) Carbohydrate catabolism in bivalves. In P. W. Hochachka (ed.), *The Mollusca.* Vol. 1. Metabolic Biochemistry and Molecular Biomechanics, Academic Press, New York, pp. 137-175.

You should be able to find this book in your local library, book store, dive shop, aquarium shop, pet store, or public aquarium. If you cannot find it locally, please contact:

Published by
Ricordea Publishing
Miami, Florida, USA
Tel 305 477.1150 Fax 305 477.5650

Distributed by
Two Little Fishies, Inc.
4016 El Prado Blvd.,
Coconut Grove, Florida, 33133 USA
Tel 305 661.7742 Fax 305 661.0611
eMail: info@twolittlefishies.com
Website: www.twolittlefishies.com